BENET'S

ARTEFACTS OF ENGLAND & THE UNITED KINGDOM

CURRENT VALUES

Millennium Second Edition 2003 AD

Compiled by Paul G. Murawski

BENET'S ARTEFACTS OF ENGLAND & THE UNITED KINGDOM CURRENT VALUES 2nd EDITION

Copyright P. G. Murawski

Published by:
Paul G. Murawski
9 Market Place
Ely
Cambridgeshire
CB7 4NP
Tel: 01353 654080
www.historyforsale.co.uk

Pre-Print Production By:
Greenlight Publishing,
The Publishing House,
119, Newland Street,
Witham,
ESSEX,
CM8 1WF

Printed By:
Printwise (Haverhill) Ltd,
Homefield Road,
Haverhill,
SUFFOLK
CB9 8QP

Cover By:
Vincent Design,
The Old Bakehouse,
49, Vinery Road,
CAMBRIDGE,
CB1 3DN

ISBN No.: 0-9536172-1-1

Jacket Illustration
Picture of a fine old British Antiquity

ii

CONTENTS

iii

CONTENTS CONTINUED

INTRODUCTION

If this is your first introduction to Benet's - welcome. If you were disappointed in not being able to obtain a copy of the sold out first edition, we hope that this edition (which has an additional 1,000 photographs with a complete revision of the values contained in the first edition) will give you information and pleasure.

If you are one of the many who contacted us with positive feedback about the first edition - thank you. Your response has spurred us on to record and photograph these additional 1,000 finds and produce this second edition which is double the size of the first.

Since the publication of the first edition of Benet's, many more finds liaison officers have been appointed around the country to deal with and record the increasing number of artefacts found by metal detectorists. The Treasure Act has enabled museums to acquire more items than previously thus reducing the amount of artefacts available to private collectors. This of course has had the knock on effect of increased values in some areas of collecting. Many of the objects photographed in Benet's have been recorded with an appropriate authority and we always encourage finders to have their finds recorded.

As stated before, Benet's is not an academic study nor an archaeological report of objects discovered and this is reflected in the brief verbal descriptions. It is instead a visual guide for initial identification purposes thus to enable finders in particular, having identified the class of the artefact, to undertake further research into their find amongst the many excellent publications which specialise in one class of artefact or another. Please note that the number of entries of one class of artefact does not indicate rarity or otherwise.

Benet's is also a guide to current market prices and is based upon first hand knowledge and experience of the antiquities market as well as knowledge of the actual prices obtained on many of the items shown. This knowledge has been combined with consultation with other experienced and respected dealers in antiquities.

We look forward with your continuing support to producing many future editions of Benet's.

ACKNOWLEDGEMENTS

This second edition has become possible due to the continuing efforts of thousands of men and women throughout the country who pursue the hobbies of field-walking and metal detecting in all weathers. Without their patience and perseverance, research and self-education, we would not have had access to such a vast and varied array of artefacts - some of great monetary value, others less so, but all of equal qualification for inclusion in this book and all of historical interest.

As stated in the Introduction, my thanks go out to the many thousands of people who purchased the first edition of Benet's and therefore made this second edition possible.

Once again, I am grateful for the professionalism and efficiency with which Alan Golbourn and his team at Greenlight Publishing carried out the pre-print production.

My warmest thanks to our great friends Robin and Claire Keeley for their total support throughout this labour of love as well as for their unqualified friendship.

My greatest thanks are to my wife Anne without whose moral support and hard work alongside me this second edition would not have been possible.

ARRANGEMENT AND REFERENCES

Artefacts have been firstly grouped into period and these periods run chronologically within the book, commencing with the Stone Age and ending with the post-Tudor period. The reference number of each artefact is prefixed by a letter of the alphabet signifying to which era the artefact belongs. We show below the reference letter of each era and the order in which they are arranged within the book:

S	STONE AGE	A	ANGLO SAXON
B	BRONZE AGE	V	VIKING
I	IRON AGE	M	MEDIEVAL & TUDOR
R	ROMAN	P	POST TUDOR

Following one of the above letters, is a two digit number which signifies the class of artefact, as follows:

01	AXES	15	HORSE & RIDER FITTINGS
02	ARROWHEADS	16	SEALS
03	SPEARS	17	KEYS & LOCKS
04	SWORDS, DAGGERS	18	WEIGHTS & MEASURES
	& KNIVES	19	WRITING IMPLEMENTS
05	OTHER WEAPONRY	20	BELLS & WHISTLES
06	PINS	21	FOOD, DRINK & DOMESTIC
07	BROOCHES		WARE
08	PENDANTS & BADGES	22	MEDICAL IMPLEMENTS
09	MOUNTS	23	TOKENS, JETONS &
10	RINGS & JEWELLERY		PLAYTHINGS
11	STATUES & FIGURINES	24	PILGRIM &
12	STRAP-ENDS & BUCKLES		RELIGIOUS ITEMS
13	CLOTHES FASTENERS	25	THIMBLES & PURSE BARS
14	COSMETIC IMPLEMENTS	99	OTHER ITEMS

Each of the above classes of artefact appears in numerical order within each age section. Thus S01 - prefixes are followed by S02 - prefixes and so on.

Thus:

A reference number commencing S02 - would signify a Stone Age arrowhead.
A reference number commencing R07 - would signify a Roman brooch.
A reference number commencing M10 - would signify a Medieval ring.

And so on.

After the above alpha/numeric prefix, there is a hyphen which is followed by a further 4 digit number which has no significance to the reader other than to pertain to one particular example of artefact within the age/class group.

VALUES

The prices shown represent the price that a collector or museum should pay for the item and NOT what a dealer in Antiquities should be expected to pay. Nor do the prices shown reflect what may occur at auction as auction prices are notoriously volatile and unpredictable.

The prices are relevant to the actual object shown. If you have an artefact in better or worse condition then the value should be adjusted accordingly.

The value of an artefact is based upon the following:

1. RARITY
2. CONDITION
3. DEMAND

You may have the rarest object in the land but if there is no demand its value would be lower. Likewise you may have a fairly common item but if it is currently in great demand and its condition is superb, its value would be higher.

STONE AGE BRITAIN

Several hundred thousand years ago, a time span that defies our total comprehension, this planet saw the dawn of what man later referred to as the Stone Age. 'Stone Age' is a rather artificial division used by previous generations of historians to describe the period during which man's tools and implements were adapted or fashioned from stone. That era before man had learnt to find, fashion and use metal of any kind.

The very earliest Stone years were labelled by early historians as the Eolithic period, from the Greek words "eos" meaning dawn and "lithos" meaning stone. Eolithic artefacts can be difficult to identify due to their very crudeness.

The subsequent Paleolithic period was so named from the Greek word "palaios" meaning ancient and once again we see the use of the word "lithos" for stone. Now imagine a club-sandwich of soil several metres below your feet. Each layer bears the traces of the lives of those who trod that soil before you. Your most recent ancestors would be nearest your feet. Your most ancient would be farthest away. Hence the meanings of the further sub-divisions of this period, namely lower Palaeolithic, Middle Palaeolithic and Upper palaeolithic - lower being the oldest. As the Palaeolithic period spanned several hundred thousand years, as would be expected during so many generations in human time, Palaeolithic artefacts vary from crudely worked flint or quartz stones to the later more sophisticated palaeoliths.

The Mesolithic period (Greek "meso" meaning middle) comes after the Palaeolithic but before the Neolithic (Greek "neos" meaning new). This narrow Mesolithic period spanned roughly 8,000 to 3,500 BC in our part of Europe. During this time we know that wood was being used as weapon and tool handles. Our Stone Age ancestors were also using wood to craft boats and paddles. From the even shorter Neolithic period, dating roughly from 3,500 to 2,000 BC, there is evidence of pottery, the weaving of material and signs of animal husbandry.

For as long as there has been man, there have been artefacts. Prehistoric hunters left behind them the surviving hard parts of arrows, bows, spears and axes made from flint or other stone. Stone Age artefacts vary from the multipurpose hand axe (which served its prehistoric masters from 2 million years ago to just 2 thousand years ago!) to the far more sophisticated array of Neolithic weapons and tools which included saws with teeth, drills, awls, picks and chisels. Neolithic man had all but perfected stone technology for, where his Palaeolithic ancestors were content with chipping off large, broad chunks around the edge of the stone, he now created artefacts by chipping, grinding, pecking and polishing.

Fresh examples of the artefacts of our Stone Age ancestors do not come onto the market with as much regularity as their later, metal counterparts. And until such time as a machine is invented to detect Stone artefacts still languishing beneath our feet, this situation will continue. Meanwhile, the only detectors capable of locating such fresh material are the keen eyes of archaelogists and field walkers or perhaps of detectorists who accidentally locate a Stone artefact whilst digging for machine indicated metal!

S01-0101
Palaeolithic Handaxe
175mm
Large and perfect example with a provenance.

£200 - £300

S01-0102
Palaeolithic Axe
135mm
Blade intact. Undamaged.

£125 - £175

S01-0103
Palaeolithic Axe
175mm
Crude worked example. A little damage.

£80 - £100

S01-0104
Palaeolithic Handaxe
135mm
Pretty honey colour.
£80 - £100

S01-0105
Palaeolithic Axe
225mm
Complete and undamaged.
Scarce.
£150 - £190

S01-0106
Palaeolithic Axe (Large)
200mm
Very large, perfect condition
and rare.
£600 - £800

S01-0107
Mesolithic
Thames Pick
125mm
Of typical style.
£50 - £70

S01-0108
Palaeolithic Handaxe
132mm
Pretty colour. Pear shape.
£150 - £180

S01-0109
Palaeolithic Ovate Handaxe
90mm
Nicely worked.
£70 - £90

S01-0110
Palaeolithic Ovate Handaxe
101mm
Good, complete example.
£100 - £125

S01-0111
Palaeolithic Handaxe
122mm
With some cortex remaining.
£75 - £85

S01-0112
Palaeolithic Handaxe
120mm
Irregular.
Some cortex remaining.
£120 - £140

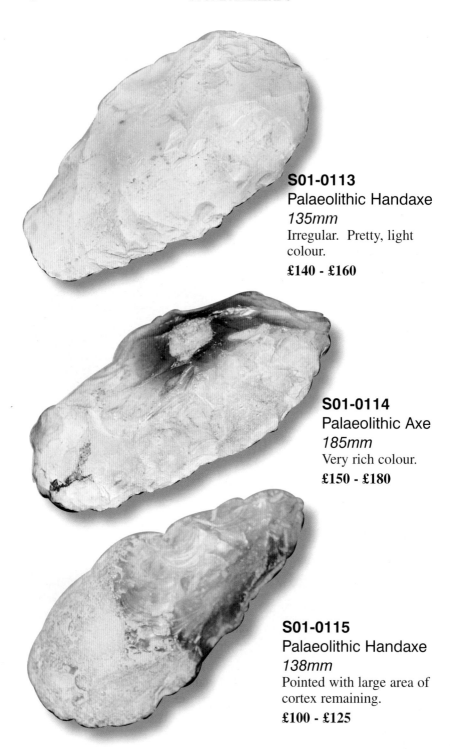

S01-0113
Palaeolithic Handaxe
135mm
Irregular. Pretty, light
colour.
£140 - £160

S01-0114
Palaeolithic Axe
185mm
Very rich colour.
£150 - £180

S01-0115
Palaeolithic Handaxe
138mm
Pointed with large area of
cortex remaining.
£100 - £125

S01-0116
Palaeolithic Axe
95mm
Well worked.
£60 - £80

S01-0117
Palaeolithic Handaxe
143mm
Pointed. Nice pale colour.
£160 - £180

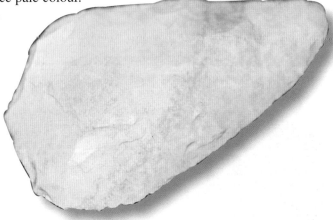

S01-0201
Neolithic Polished
Axehead
250mm
Finest example. Superb
colour. Very large.
£500 - £900

S01-0202
Neolithic Polished
Axehead
90mm
£50 - £75

S01-0203
Neolithic Polished
Stone Axe
145mm
Highly polished.
£75 - £150

S01-0204
Neolithic
Polished
Axehead
155mm
Slight chip to the
cutting edge.
£50 - £70

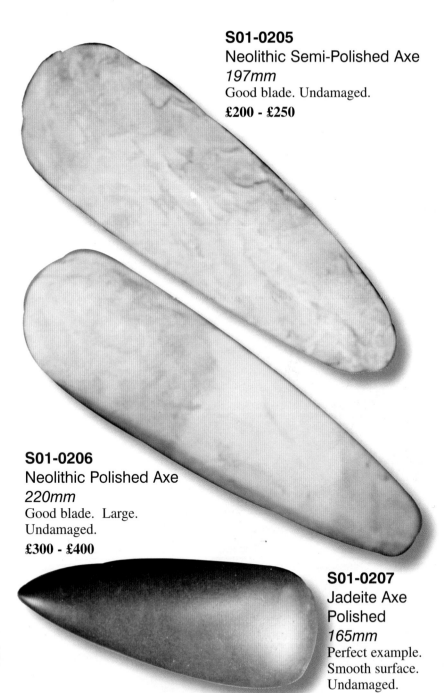

S01-0205
Neolithic Semi-Polished Axe
197mm
Good blade. Undamaged.
£200 - £250

S01-0206
Neolithic Polished Axe
220mm
Good blade. Large.
Undamaged.
£300 - £400

S01-0207
Jadeite Axe
Polished
165mm
Perfect example.
Smooth surface.
Undamaged.
From £2,000

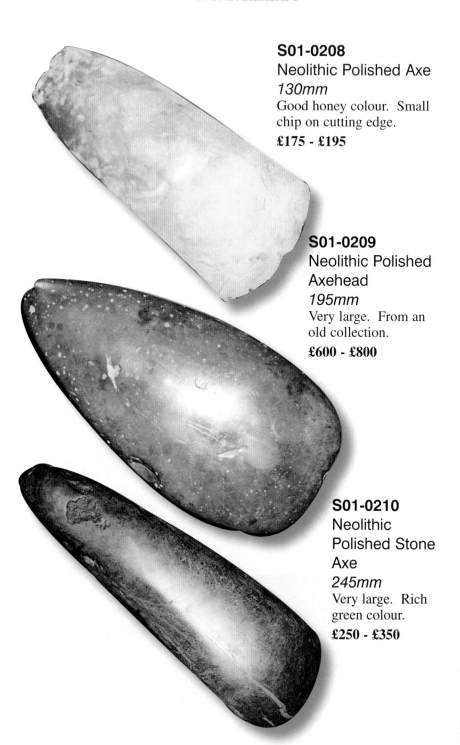

S01-0208
Neolithic Polished Axe
130mm
Good honey colour. Small
chip on cutting edge.
£175 - £195

S01-0209
Neolithic Polished
Axehead
195mm
Very large. From an
old collection.
£600 - £800

S01-0210
Neolithic
Polished Stone
Axe
245mm
Very large. Rich
green colour.
£250 - £350

S01-0211
Neolithic Axehead
102mm
Grainy surface.
£50 - £75

S01-0212
Neolithic Axehead (Greenstone)
95mm
Complete and undamaged.
£70 - £80

S01-0213
Axehead
135mm
Well worked. Dark flint.
£90 - £120

S01-0214
Neolithic Axe (Polished)
98mm
Highly polished and
complete.
£150 - £175

S01-0215
Neolithic Axe
(Polished)
100mm
Nicely polished and
complete.
£160 - £180

S01-0216
Neolithic Axehead
170mm
Large and complete.
£150 - £175

S01-0217
Neolithic Axehead
146mm
Polished with a good cutting edge.
£180 - £200

S01-0218
Neolithic Axe
125mm
Nicely worked.
Undamaged.
£180 - £225

S01-0219
Neolithic Axehead
132mm
Milky white. Perfect cutting edge.
£250 - £275

S01-0220
Neolithic Axe
220mm
Very large. Damage
to cutting edge.
£300 - £400

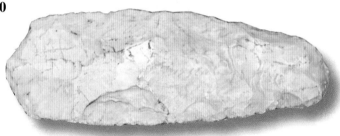

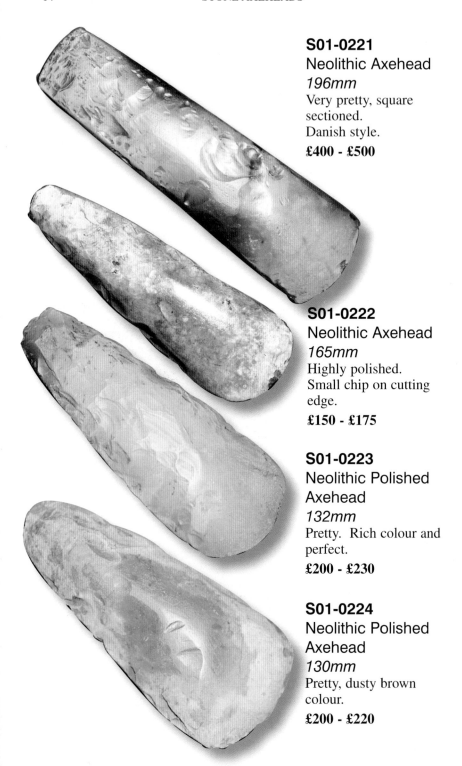

S01-0221
Neolithic Axehead
196mm
Very pretty, square
sectioned.
Danish style.
£400 - £500

S01-0222
Neolithic Axehead
165mm
Highly polished.
Small chip on cutting
edge.
£150 - £175

S01-0223
Neolithic Polished
Axehead
132mm
Pretty. Rich colour and
perfect.
£200 - £230

S01-0224
Neolithic Polished
Axehead
130mm
Pretty, dusty brown
colour.
£200 - £220

S01-0301
Neolithic Hand Axe
120mm
Standard type.
£50 - £95

S01-0302
Neolithic Flint Axehead
130mm
Mottled colour. Some polishing.
£80 - £150

S01-0303
Neolithic Flint Axehead
132mm
Sharp cutting edge. Polished.
£100 - £150

S01-0304
Neolithic Flaked Flint Axe
125mm
Nicely worked example.
£100 - £150

S01-0305
Neolithic Thin-Butted Axe
180mm
Scarcer type. Polished.
£150 - £250

S01-0306
Neolithic Axe
150mm
Undamaged.
£150 - £200

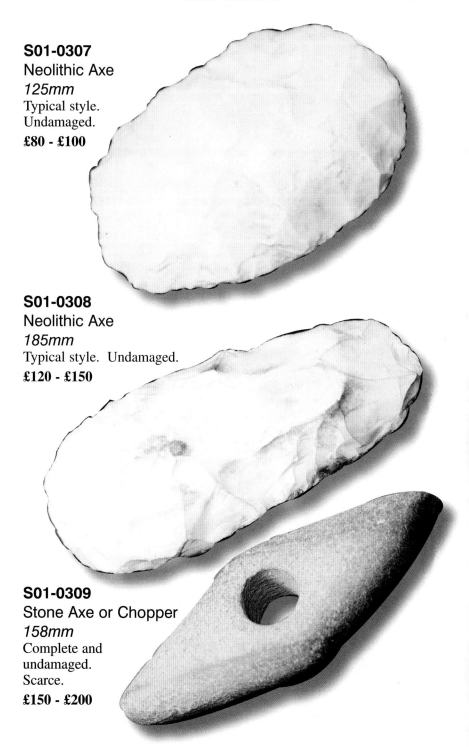

S01-0307
Neolithic Axe
125mm
Typical style.
Undamaged.
£80 - £100

S01-0308
Neolithic Axe
185mm
Typical style. Undamaged.
£120 - £150

S01-0309
Stone Axe or Chopper
158mm
Complete and
undamaged.
Scarce.
£150 - £200

S01-0310
Stone Axe or
Chopper
190mm
Large example.
£150 - £200

S01-0311
Neolithic Flint
Axehead (Splayed)
138mm
Perfect in every respect
and provenanced.
£300 - £350

S01-0312
Neolithic Axehead
145mm
Small chip to cutting
edge.
£180 - £230

S01-0313
Neolithic Axe
230mm
Very large grainy finish.
£250 - £300

S01-0314
Neolithic Axehead
165mm
Nicely worked.
Undamaged.
£225 - £275

S02-0101
Neolithic Arrowheads
Basic examples.
£15 each

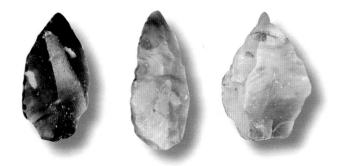

S02-0102
Neolithic
Arrowheads
Basic examples.
£10 each

S02-0103
Neolithic Leaf-Shaped
Arrowhead
40mm
Point broken.
£15

S02-0104
Neolithic Leaf-Shaped
Arrowhead
50mm
Standard type.
£30

S02-0105
Neolithic Leaf-Shaped Arrowhead
55mm
Standard type.
£30

S02-0106
Neolithic Leaf-Shaped Arrowhead
45mm
Standard type.
£30

S02-0107
Neolithic Arrowhead
57mm
Very large.
£40 - £60

S02-0108
Neolithic Leaf-Shaped Arrowhead
30mm
Standard type.
£30

S02-0109
Neolithic Leaf-
Shaped Arrowhead
43mm
Large size.
£40

S02-0110
Neolithic Arrowhead
35mm
Standard type.
£35

S02-0111
Neolithic Arrowhead
42mm
Standard type.
£35

S02-0112
Neolithic Tranchet
Arrowhead
27mm
Scarcer type.
£25

S02-0113
Neolithic Arrowhead
30mm
Beautifully worked.
£40

S02-0201
Bronze Age Barbed &
Tanged Arrowhead
32mm
Complete and undamaged.
£50 - 60

S02-0202
Bronze Age Barbed & Tanged
Arrowhead
23mm
Perfect and undamaged.
£70

S02-0203
Barbed & Tanged Arrowhead
33mm
Small piece missing from tip.
£50

S02-0204
Bronze Age Barbed &
Tanged Arrowhead
37mm
Large and perfect. Provenanced.
£120

S04-0101
Neolithic Knife
110mm
Undamaged.
£30 - £50

S04-0102
Neolithic Flint
Knife
105mm
Slight damage.
£20 - £40

S04-0103
Neolithic Knife
95mm
Nicely worked and
undamaged.
£90 - £120

S04-0104
Neolithic Knife
80mm
Perfect and undamaged.
Some cortex.
£90 - £120

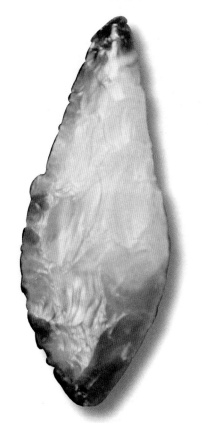

S04-0201
Beaker Dagger
162mm
Complete and
undamaged. Rare.
£500 - £600

S04-0202
Dagger
160mm
Large size.
£150 - £180

S99-0101
Neolithic Leaf Shaped
Point
44mm
Basic type.
£10

S99-0102
Neolithic Leaf Shaped
Point
50mm
Basic type.
£15

S99-0103
Neolithic Leaf Shaped
Point
52mm
Basic type.
£15

S99-0104
Neolithic Leaf Shaped
Point
50mm
Nicely worked.
£35

S99-0201
Neolithic Scrapers
Worked edges.
£10 each

S99-0202
Neolithic Chisel
175mm
Large and rare
£130 - £160

S99-0301
Neolithic Boring Tool
130mm
Scarcer item.
£30 - £50

S99-0401
Neolithic Mace
Head
90mm (dia)
Scarcer item.
£50 - £75

S99-0402
Neolithic Mace
Head
85mm
Smooth, even surface.
£60 - £80

S99-0403
Neolithic Mace
Head
77mm
Doughnut type.
£50 - £75

S99-0404
Neolithic Mace Head
(Round)
75mm
Round with indentations.
£50 - £75

BRONZE AGE BRITAIN

Bronze is an alloy (mixture) of the two metals copper and tin. The reason why Britain did not experience a Copper Age (or even Tin Age!) is that by the time that metal technology had reached these shores, man had already worked out that bronze was harder than either of its components which, on their own, could not successfully be used as weapons or tools. Bronze weapons and tools, together with the knowledge of their manufacture, infiltrated different areas of Britain from the Continent over decades and centuries. But, if we were to put an arbitrary date on the commencement of the British Bronze Age it would, coincidentally, be as far on the other side of the birth of Christ as we are on this side. Thus the period around 2,000 BC saw British bronze artefacts taking their place alongside stone artefacts, for the inception of one technology does not immediately eradicate an earlier technology. Likewise, the end of the late British Bronze Age of 1,000 to 400 BC saw the inception of the British Iron Age, but not the eradication of the use of bronze.

Although the British Bronze Age flourished in part due to a wealth of local resources (namely the tin of Cornwall and the copper of Ireland), stone continued to be used in the form of beautifully chipped hammers and arrowheads. In some areas copper was used on its own for personal ornamentation, and gold was definitely used by the Late Bronze Age either, like copper, for self-decoration or to embellish precious weapons. However, due to the rarity of non-bronze artefacts from this period, our Bronze Age section will of necessity comprise bronze artefacts.

Bronze Age hoards have been an enormous source of information about this period of British prehistory. Finds have included hoards of broken or damaged weapons and tools, perhaps to be recast by their owner or, if he had not mastered the technology, to be traded with the next itinerant bronze-worker to call. These bronze-workers, or founders, also unintentionally left well buried hoards to be unearthed millenia later. These hoards could comprise unworked pieces of bronze or unfinished articles as well as broken or faulty items for recast. Who knows what happened to the founder who was unable to return and retrieve his stock-in-trade?

Apart from these prehistoric examples of recycling, Bronze Age bronze artefacts turn up in limited quantities as burial finds. But it is unfortunate that at this time the tradition of cremation of artefacts with their deceased owner greatly reduced this source of artefacts. Apart from hoards and limited burial finds, individual objects, not hidden but lost by their Bronze Age owner, continue to be turned up by the plough and found by the metal detector.

The main criteria for obtaining the best price for a Bronze Age artefact from Britain is a smooth, even patina and an undamaged condition. Spears, in good condition, tend to be more popular than axes. The palstave type of axe tends to be more popular amongst collectors than the looped and socketed examples.

B01-0101
Looped & Socketed Axe
65mm
Plain axehead, slight pitting
and a little damage to blade.
Small size.
£50 - £75

B01-0102
Looped & Socketed Axe
100mm
Plain axehead, very little
pitting on surface. Blade a
little ragged.
£75 - £100

B01-0103
Looped & Socketed Axe
102mm
Plain axehead, undamaged,
slight pitting on surface.
Large size.
£150 - £195

B01-0104
Looped & Socketed Axe
90mm
Very lightly decorated
axehead, single band near the
top, slight pitting.
£110 - £175

B01-0105
Looped & Socketed
Axe
101mm
Lightly decorated axehead
with single band near the
top. Blade a little ragged.
£80 - £150

B01-0106
Looped & Socketed
Axe
95mm
Decorated with a single
band near the top. Very
little pitting. Flared blade.
£90 - £160

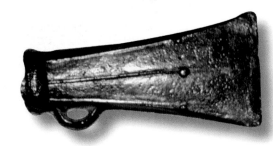

B01-0107
Looped & Socketed
Decorated Axehead
120mm
Very high tin content.
Line and pellet decoration.
Good condition.
£100 - £175

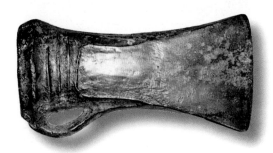

B01-0108
Looped & Socketed
Axe
92mm
Decorated axehead of
typical European style.
Light pitting.
£70 - £140

B01-0109
Looped & Socketed
Decorated Axe
110mm
Very lightly decorated,
corrosion around blade
area. Chunky.
£75 - £125

B01-0110
Looped & Socketed
Decorated Axe
107mm
Light decoration, blade
undamaged, small scuff on
surface.
£70 - £140

B01-0111
Looped & Socketed
Decorated Axe
110mm
Flared socket, linear
decoration. Pitted.
Blade a little ragged.
£65 - £125

B01-0112
Looped & Socketed
Decorated Axe
140mm
Perfect axehead. Linear
decoration. Very large with
superb patination.
£300 - £450

B01-0113
Looped & Socketed
Decorated Axe
102mm
Short linear decoration.
Blade a little ragged.
£70 - £130

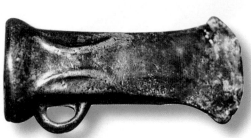

B01-0114
Looped & Socketed
Decorated Axe
102mm
Decorated axehead.
Slight tin content.
Corrosion around the
blade.
£75 - £110

B01-0115
Looped & Socketed
Decorated Axe
102mm
Decorated axehead.
Slight tin content.
Corrosion around the
blade.
£75 - £125

B01-0116
Looped & Socketed
Decorated Axe
104mm
Decorated axehead.
Slightly pitted. Blade
uneven.
£75 - £125

B01-0117
Looped & Socketed
Axe Light Decoration
103mm
Complete. Patina a little
uneven.
£80 - £120

B01-0118
Looped & Socketed
Decorated Axe
125mm
Linear decoration.
Very large with
superb patination.
£300 - £350

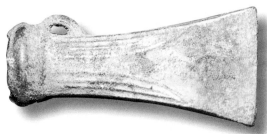

B01-0119
Looped & Socketed
Decorated Axe
105mm
Decorated axehead.
Linear decoration. Even
patination.
£150 - £180

B01-0201
Palstave Axe
145mm
Plain. Blade a little uneven. Patina patchy.
£120 - £180

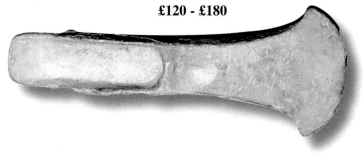

B01-0202
Palstave Axe
142mm
Superb blade. Shield decoration.
Lovely brown patina.
£250 - £350

B01-0203
Palstave Looped Axe
130mm
Central rib decoration.
Patina flaking. Blade
chipped.
£100 - £150

B01-0204
Palstave Axe
165mm
Centre rib. Good,
smooth surface.
Even patina.
Undamaged.
£400 - £500

B01-0205
Winged Palstave
160mm
Even patina. Blade
undamaged.
£200 - £250

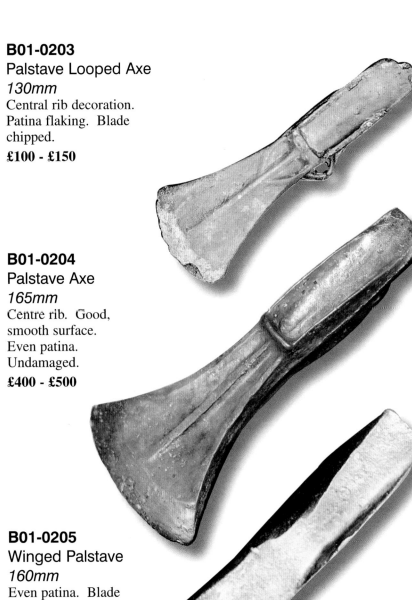

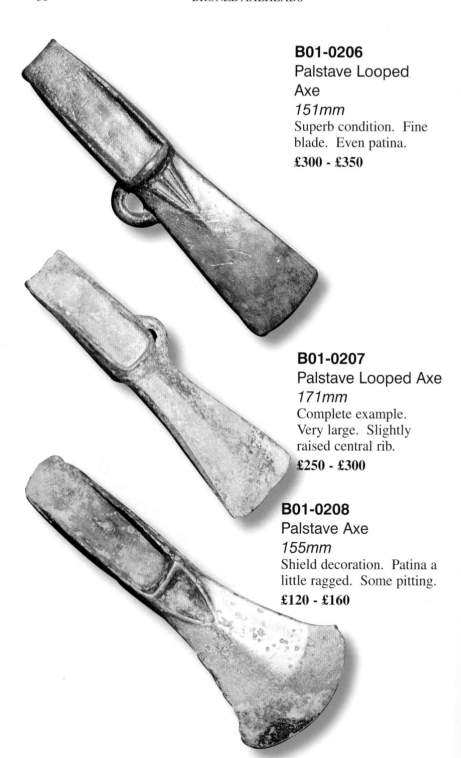

B01-0206
Palstave Looped Axe
151mm
Superb condition. Fine blade. Even patina.
£300 - £350

B01-0207
Palstave Looped Axe
171mm
Complete example. Very large. Slightly raised central rib.
£250 - £300

B01-0208
Palstave Axe
155mm
Shield decoration. Patina a little ragged. Some pitting.
£120 - £160

B01-0301
Flanged Axe
90mm
Pitted surface.
Patina flaking.
£75 - £130

B01-0302
Flanged Axe
84mm
Good example.
Even patina.
Blade intact.
£100 - £180

B01-0303
Flanged Axe
110mm
Good, even patina.
Blade undamaged.
£300 - £350

B01-0304
Flanged Axe
Decorated
131mm
Flared blade.
Even patina.
£300 - £350

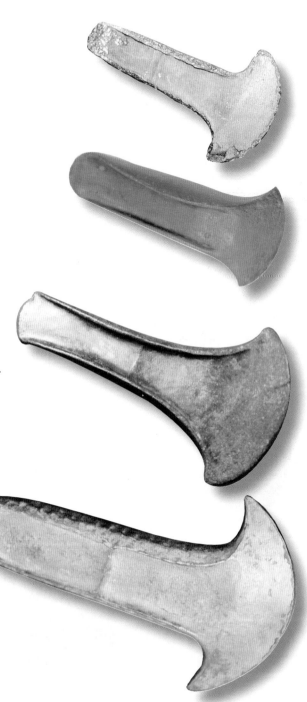

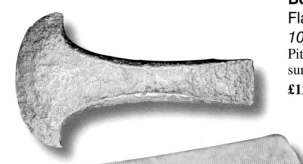

B01-0305
Flanged Axe
100mm
Pitted and uneven
surface.

£125 - £150

B01-0401
Flat Axe
114mm
Plain example.
Surface a little pitted.
Scarce.

£150 - £200

B01-0402
Flat Axe
75mm
Very nice example.
Smooth, even surface.
Good cutting edge.

£180 - £225

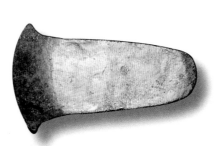

B01-0403
Flat Axe
110mm
Plain example.
Surface a little rough.

£140 - £160

B03-0101
Socketed Spearhead
200mm
Pitted surface. Late type,
maybe into Iron Age. Large
example.
£90 - £150

B03-0102
Socketed Spearhead
190mm
Sound patina. Good blade.
£150 - £225

B03-0103
Socketed Spearhead
120mm
Point broken and restored.
Leaf shape blade.
£80 - £130

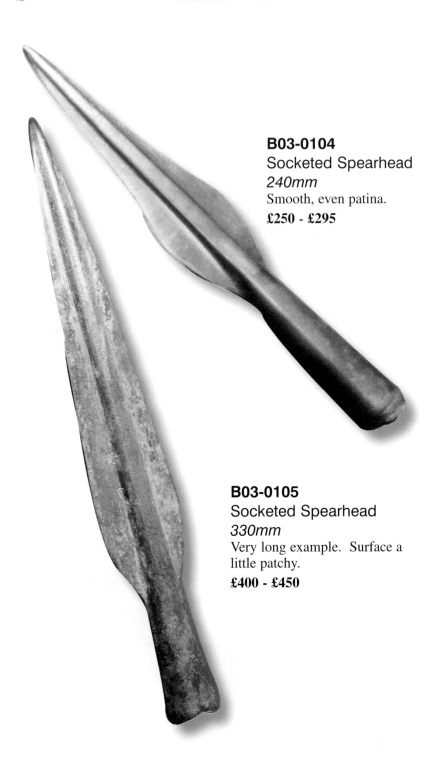

B03-0104
Socketed Spearhead
240mm
Smooth, even patina.
£250 - £295

B03-0105
Socketed Spearhead
330mm
Very long example. Surface a
little patchy.
£400 - £450

B03-0106
Socketed Spearhead
185mm
Good, large example. A
little pitting in places.
£120 - £175

B03-0107
Socketed Spearhead
160mm
Uneven surface. Traces of
wood still in shaft.
Central raised rib.
£100 - £140

B03-0201
Socketed Peg Type
Spearhead
137mm
Slight pitting. A little
damage to blade.
£75 - £125

B03-0202
Socketed Peg Type
Spearhead
220mm
Sound patina. Undamaged.
Good example. Large.
£180 - £275

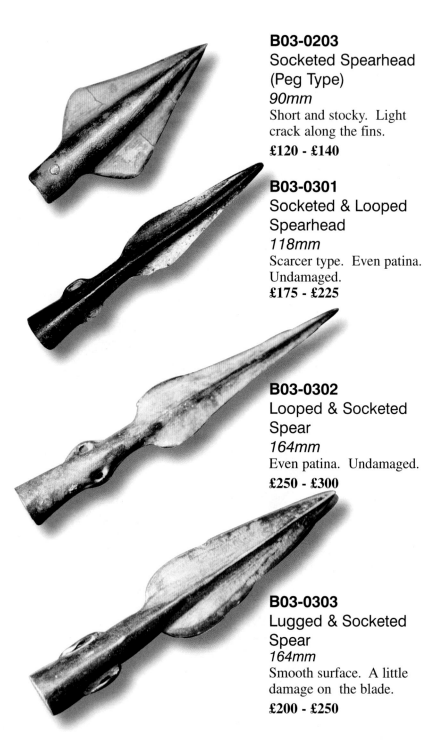

B03-0203
Socketed Spearhead
(Peg Type)
90mm
Short and stocky. Light
crack along the fins.
£120 - £140

B03-0301
Socketed & Looped
Spearhead
118mm
Scarcer type. Even patina.
Undamaged.
£175 - £225

B03-0302
Looped & Socketed
Spear
164mm
Even patina. Undamaged.
£250 - £300

B03-0303
Lugged & Socketed
Spear
164mm
Smooth surface. A little
damage on the blade.
£200 - £250

B03-0304
Looped & Socketed Spear
100mm
Small. Patina a little uneven.
Damage to the blade.
£100 - £130

B04-0101
Dagger or Knife Blade
148mm
Smooth, even patination.
Long length.
£80 - £100

B04-0102
Dagger Blade
138mm
Even, green patination.
Fluted decoration.
Blade a little ragged.
£225 - £275

B04-0103
Dagger Blade
190mm
Large example. Smooth,
even green patination.
£300 - £400

B04-0104
Dagger Blade
153mm
Surface a little ragged,
both rivet holes in place
£100 - £150

B04-0201
Bronze Sword
Complete
560mm
Good, even patina.
Complete.
From £1,500

B14-0601

Razor

130mm

Surface a little pitted.
Sharp cutting edge.

£120 - £150

B14-0602

Razor

84mm

Decorated. Even green
patination.

£80 - £100

B14-0603

Razor

63mm

Open-work. Bell shape.
Pendant type.

£120 - £150

B99-0101

Socketed Gouge

90mm

A little ragged over the
surface.

£50 - £95

B99-0102

Socketed Gouge

101mm

Even patina.
Fragment broken at
the back.

£40 - £65

B99-0103
Socketed Gouge
101mm
Pitted surface. Blade
a little ragged.
£50 - £95

B99-0104
Socketed Gouge
97mm
Very slight pitting.
Ragged blade.
£50 - £95

B99-0105
Socketed Gouge
82mm
Corrosion around the
blade. Attractive
patina.
£60 - £90

B99-0106
Socketed Gouge
82mm
Pleasant example.
Light pitting.
£60 - £95

B99-0201
Tanged Chisel
105mm
Slight damage to the
blade.
£50 - £75

B99-0202
Tanged Chisel
65mm
Smooth, even patina.
Undamaged.
£60 - £80

B99-0203
Chisel
102mm
Slight chip in blade.
£50 - £75

B99-0301
Hammer
75mm
Some tin content. Scarce
item.
£100 - £180

B99-0501
Hoard
Provenanced and
recorded with a
museum.
£600 - £850

B99-0502
Hoard
Provenanced. Mainly broken objects.
£150 - £200

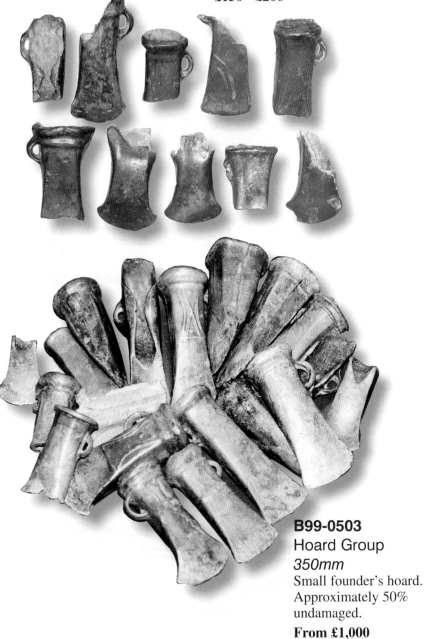

B99-0503
Hoard Group
350mm
Small founder's hoard.
Approximately 50%
undamaged.
From £1,000

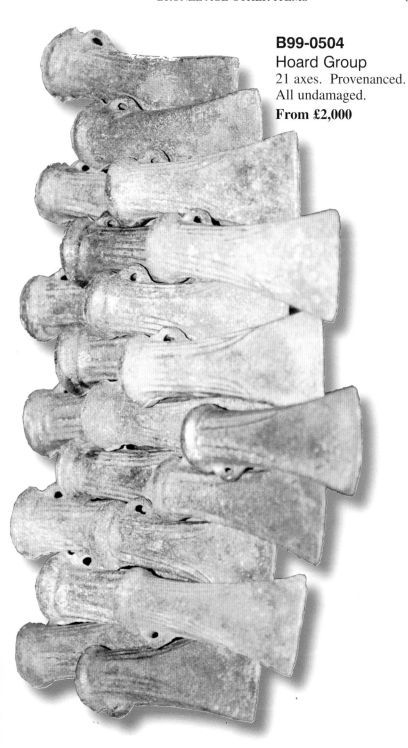

B99-0504
Hoard Group
21 axes. Provenanced.
All undamaged.
From £2,000

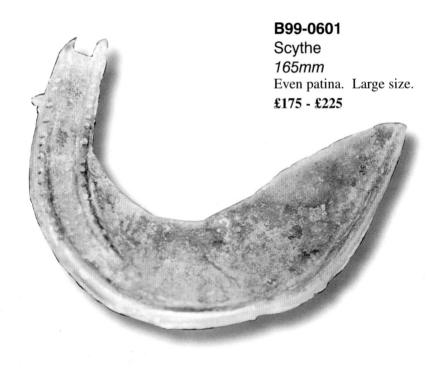

B99-0601
Scythe
165mm
Even patina. Large size.
£175 - £225

B99-0602
Scythe
210mm
Large example.
Continental type.
£100 - £120

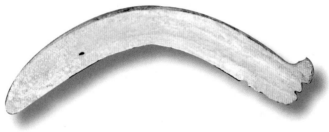

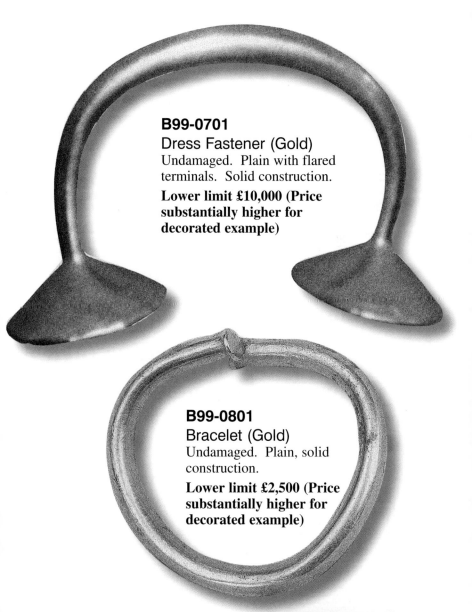

B99-0701
Dress Fastener (Gold)
Undamaged. Plain with flared terminals. Solid construction.

Lower limit £10,000 (Price substantially higher for decorated example)

B99-0801
Bracelet (Gold)
Undamaged. Plain, solid construction.

Lower limit £2,500 (Price substantially higher for decorated example)

B99-0901
Gold Ring
22mm dia
Triple banded. Undamaged.
£400 - £500

54

THE CELTIC IRON AGE

Iron was known in the Middle East as long ago as 4,000 BC where the earliest iron objects, made from meteoric iron, have been found. Small wonder then that the very word 'iron' derives from the phrase "metal from the sky" in various early languages. At first iron was worked cold but, by 1,500 BC, the people of the Middle East were smelting iron from the ore and had learned that by the process of heating and hammering, such "wrought" metal was not only more accurately shaped but was also greatly toughened. This knowledge of wrought iron was a closely guarded secret amongst the Hittites (modern Turkey) until about 1,200 BC when this knowledge spread through Greece and Italy into the rest of Europe.

By 800 BC, the Celts of western Europe, a proud and artistic but fiercely tribal people, had adopted the working and use of iron, becoming highly proficient in developing more technical tools and farming implements as well as more hardy daggers, knives and swords. During the last half of the millenium BC, knowledge of the working of iron in these islands spread from region to region together with the gradual infiltration of Celtic technology, farming skills, culture, art and language by trade, immigration and, no doubt, the occasional local bout of hostile invasion.

Once again, the name of the age does not preclude the usage of pre-existing materials and bronze continued to be used where it was more serviceable such as mounts for iron weapons and tools, as handles or scabbards and, of course, as highly stylized jewellery. As well as bronze, gold continued to adorn the bodies and artefacts solely of those of greatest social importance. Thus, our Iron Age section will not be confined to ferrous material!

An important element of Celtic Iron Age metalwork was the skilful application of enamel to metal. Vivid reds and yellows enliven such diverse artefacts as horse trappings, shields and brooches. A dash of blue can embellish a bronze dagger hilt above an iron blade. Nor was Celtic art in metal-work confined to colour. Shape and form were indulged to the point of disproportion and misrepresentation. No classical features here of a face being a face or a horse a horse. Instead we have to closely examine the spirals and tendrils, the loops and wavy lines and, only then, does the shape of a creature come to us. Celtic art, as applied to Iron Age artefacts, is also an expression of our ancestors' religion and spirituality.

Religious practises of our Celtic ancestors supply us with artefacts today, whether we find votive deposits consigned to a spring imbued with magical qualities or whether we unearth a Celtic inhumation at a place or in a period when cremation was not in favour.

There is a strong following at the moment for good quality Celtic artefacts, their value determined by the beauty and consistency of the patina, the amount and quality of enamelling as well as the standard of metallurgical artwork.

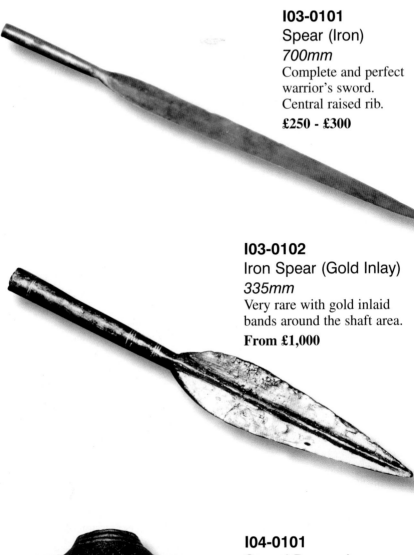

I03-0101
Spear (Iron)
700mm
Complete and perfect
warrior's sword.
Central raised rib.
£250 - £300

I03-0102
Iron Spear (Gold Inlay)
335mm
Very rare with gold inlaid
bands around the shaft area.
From £1,000

I04-0101
Sword Pommel
56mm
From an Iron Age sword,
decorated with punched dot
patterns.
£150 - £225

I04-0102
Short Sword (Iron)
450mm
Complete with its pommel.
Good state of preservation.
£600 - £700

I04-0103
Short Sword (Iron)
500mm
Pommel missing but good
state of preservation.
£250 - £350

I04-0104
Sword & Scabbard
990mm
Sword complete with its
scabbard. Very long and
complete.
From £2,000

I04-0105
Sword (With Scabbard)
775mm
Sword still in its original scabbard. Slight damage to the scabbard.
£800 - £1,000

I04-0106
Sword Handle Decoration
22mm
Fully enamelled. Very vivid colours.
£70 - £80

I04-0201
Dagger Pommel
20mm
Cells of orange and white enamel. Ragged surface. Small.
£80 - £95

I04-0202
Dagger Pommel (Coral)
15mm
Small but complete.
£70 - £80

I04-0203
Dagger Pommel
22mm
Moulded triskel design with three pellets.
£60 - £75

I04-0204
Dagger
315mm
Blade a little ragged. Tang and pommel in place.
£200 - £300

I04-0301
Knife Handle
45mm
Crested head. Surface a little ragged.
£150 - £200

I04-0302
Knife Handle
47mm
Crested head. Bulbous eyes.
Surface a little ragged.
£140 - £180

I04-0303
Knife Handle
42mm
Smooth, even patination.
Incised line decoration.
£100 - £130

I04-0401
Dagger Ferrule
(Enamelled)
20mm
Vivid red and yellow
enamel.
£50 - £70

I04-0501
Scabbard Chape
45mm
From the bottom of a sword
scabbard with fixing hole.

£40 - £50

I07-0101
Brooch (Dragonesque)
45mm
Fine, animated Celtic style.
With pin.

£250 - £300

I07-0102
Brooch (Dragonesque)
40mm
Traces of enamel. Even patina. With pin.

£350 - £450

I07-0103
Brooch (Dragonesque)
50mm
Traces of enamel. Unusual
style. With pin.

£350 - £450

I07-0104
Brooch (Dragonesque)
48mm
Enamelled.   With pin.
£300 - £400

I07-0105
Brooch (Dragonesque)
Enamelled
54mm
Pin intact. Good, even patina.
Most of the enamel intact.
Large size.
£750 - £850

I07-0106
Brooch (Dragonesque)
61mm
Orange, blue and yellow enamel.
Pin missing. Large size.
£500 - £600

I07-0107
Brooch (Dragonesque)
47mm
Even green patination.
Rectangular, enamelled cells.
Complete with pin.
£500 - £600

I07-0108
Brooch (Dragonesque)
58mm
Turned up snout. Red, yellow and green enamel cells. No pin.
£250 - £300

I07-0109
Brooch (Dragonesque)
54mm
Unusual style. Triangular enamel cells. Pin missing.
£250 - £300

I07-0110
Brooch (Dragonesque)
51mm
Celtic "eye" design in the central body area. Nice, even green patina. Pin missing.
£300 - £350

I07-0111
Brooch (Dragonesque)
47mm
Surface a little ragged. Pin missing.
£130 - £175

I07-0201
Brooch (La Tene)
35mm
Complete, undamaged. Even patina.
£50 - £75

I07-0202
Brooch (La Tene II)
39mm
One piece, with globular decoration. Rare.
£40 - £60

I07-0203
Brooch (La Tene)
35mm
Complete, undamaged. Even patina.
£50 - £75

I07-0204
Brooch (La Tene)
40mm
Complete. Even, smooth green patination.
£70 - £80

I07-0205
Brooch (La Tene III)
57mm
Complete. Even green patination.
£70 - £80

I07-0301
Brooch (Violin Type)
40mm
Ring and dot decoration. Even patina. Rare type.
£60 - £80

I07-0401
Annular Brooch
31mm
Early Iron Age. Even patina.
£25 - £45

I07-0402
Celtic Brooch
70mm
Late Iron Age style. Iron pin (missing).
£50 - £70

I07-0501
Brooch
48mm
Rare early brooch
with original pin.
£150 - £200

I08-0101
Pendant (Horned God)
40mm
Suspension loop undamaged.
Sharp detail. Rare.
£100 - £150

I08-0201
Stylus Pendant (Bird)
35mm
Bronze bird with suspension
loop. (Birds feature prominent-
ly in Celtic mythology.) Rare.
£125 - £175

I08-0301
Pendant (Dagger)
67mm
Flaky chocolate brown
patination.
£80 - £100

I09-0101
Belt Mount
22mm
Enamel inlay.
£50 - £80

I09-0102
Belt Mount
27mm
La Tene "eye" looped belt decoration with enamel. Ragged
surface.
£40 - £60

I09-0103
Belt Mount
35mm
Celtic "eye" form. With
enamel.
£75 - £95

I09-0104
Belt Mount
48mm
Double Celtic "eye" type.
£40 - £50

I09-0105
Mount (Belt Slider)
39mm
Red enamel. Ragged surface.
£20 - £30

I09-0106
Belt Mount
36mm
Red enamel circle design.
Superb green patination.
£200 - £250

I09-0201
Mount
30mm
Probably a decorative mount from a
horse harness. Gruesome face.
£60 - £80

I09-0202
Mount
38mm
Typical Celtic style. Traces of
silvering.
£100 - £150

I09-0203
Mount (Celtic Deity)
40mm
Bearded bust in a cloak. Hood
over the hairstyle.
£150 - £200

I09-0204
Mount
18mm
Set within an iron
concretion. Typical Celtic
style. Small size.
£50 - £75

I09-0205
Mount
45mm
Typical Celtic style.
£80 - £100

I09-0206
Mount
50mm
Head in the centre. Four
panels of enamel and four
saltires of enamel. Rare.
£400 - £500

I09-0207
Mount
42mm
Sleeping figure. Patination a
little patchy.
£120 - £150

I09-0208
Mount
25mm
Smooth. Even, rich green
patination. Incised line
decoration.
£100 - £125

I09-0301
Boar Mount
54mm
Probably from the top of a
helmet. Undamaged. Even
patina. Rare.
£350 - £500

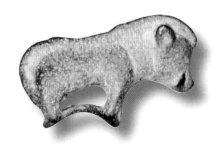

I09-0302
Mount (Horse Head)
45mm
Probably from a bucket. Surface a little ragged.
£150 - £200

I09-0303
Mount (Staff Top)
65mm
Hallstatt style. Triple horned animal. Scarce.
£300 - £375

I09-0304
Mount (Bird)
32mm
Decorated with incised lines. Even patina.
£60 - £80

I09-0305
Mount (Bulls Head)
32mm
European Iron Age. Well modelled. Surface pitted.
£150 - £200

I09-0306
Mount (Bulls Head)
45mm
Typical Celtic style. Solid construction. Surface a little ragged.
£100 - £150

I09-0307
Mount (Bulls Head)
50mm
Typical Celtic style. Hollow along the neck. Broken.
£80 - £100

I09-0308
Enamelled Mount
36mm
Spectacle type. Two fixing
spikes on reverse. Fully
enamelled.
£40 - £60

I09-0309
Mount (Hanging Bowl)
Bull
39mm
Crude style. A little damage to
one of the horns. Even patina.
£100 - £125

I09-0310
Mount (Staff Top)
58mm
Wolf-like animal with elongated
neck. Smooth, even patination.
£350 - £400

I09-0311
Mount (Bull)
50mm
Bull in lying position.
Small break to one of the
horns. Even patination. Rare.
£400 - £450

I09-0312
Mount (Bulls Head)
45mm
Large, curly horns. Even
green patination. Undamaged.
£90 - £100

I09-0313
Mount (Hanging Bowl)
62mm
Crude style of bull with two
horns.
£70 - £90

I09-0314
Mount (Bird)
48mm
Incised line decoration to
indicate the wings. Dotted
decoration for the feathers.
Surface pitted.
£150 - £200

I09-0315
Mount (Bird)
38mm
Pelleted eye. Incised lines on the wings. Smooth, even patination.
£70 - £90

I09-0316
Mount
45mm
Stylised male bust. Surface a little ragged.
£150 - £200

I09-0401
Mount (Triskele)
35mm
Typical Celtic style. Surface a little ragged.
£50 - £80

I09-0402
Mount
23mm
Two fixing studs on the rear.
Even patina.
£75 - £95

I10-0101
Gold Snake Ring
21mm dia
Coiled snake. Tail end broken.
£600 - £750

I11-0101
Rider Warrior
82mm
From a horse-and-rider group.
Crested helmet, cloak and cav-
alry tunic. Large size.
£500 - £600

I11-0102
Rider Warrior
62mm
From a horse-and-rider group.
Crested helmet. Even patina.
£450 - £550

I11-0103
Rider Warrior
52mm
From a horse-and-rider group.
Crested helmet.
Pronounced phallus.
£300 - £400

I11-0104
Rider Warrior
48mm
From a horse-and-rider group.
Crested helmet.
One leg broken.
£150 - £250

I11-0105
Votive Figurine (River Goddess)
35mm
Reclining female. Three dimensional. Rare.
£125 - £175

I11-0106
Votive Figurine (River Goddess)
30mm
Reclining female. Three dimensional. Good detail and patination.
£150 - £175

I11-0107
Rider Warrior
66mm
Cloak flying out behind. Holding a ceremonial staff. Rare.
£600 - £700

I11-0108
Boar Statuette
51mm
Patination a little ragged.
Rare.
£350 - £400

I11-0109
Captive Figure
43mm
Surface a little ragged, but a
very rare example.
£300 - £400

I13-0101
Clothes Fastener
48mm
Rectangular head with strips of
enamel. Surface flaking.
£50 - £75

I13-0102
Clothes Fastener
25mm
Enamelled, rough surface and
pitted.
£20 - £30

I13-0103
Clothes Fastener
38mm
Concentric rings with enamel.
Some pitting.
£30 - £45

I13-0104
Clothes Fastener
40mm
Celtic "eye" design.
£40 - £50

I13-0105
Clothes Fastener
32mm
Unusual spoked wheel design
with enamel.
£40 - £50

I13-0201
Clothes Fastener
36mm
Square head and devolved
Celtic design.
£30 - £40

I13-0202
Clothes Fastener
24mm
Toggle fastener. Ragged surface.
£20 - £30

I13-0203
Clothes Fastener
45mm
Button-and-loop fastener, "eye" shape.
£30 - £40

I13-0204
Clothes Fastener
42mm
Button-and-loop fastener. Domed front and triangular back loop.
£60 - £75

I13-0205
Clothes Fastener
32mm
Button-and-loop fastener. Rectangular plate. Raised dome in the centre. Smooth even patina.
£50 - £75

I13-0206
Clothes Fastener
55mm
Button-and-loop fastener. Two raised buttons. One of "eye" design.
£60 - £80

I13-0207
Clothes Fastener
27mm
Toggle type. Pitted surface.
£20 - £40

I13-0208
Clothes Fastener
20mm
"Cotton reel" toggle with loop. Scarce type.
£70 - £90

I13-0209
Clothes Fastener
(Toggle)
30mm
Surface a little pitted.
£70 - £80

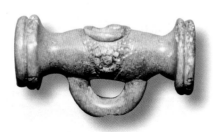

I13-0210
Clothes Fastener
28mm
Toggle type. Surface a little pitted.
£50 - £60

I13-0211
Clothes Fastener
38mm
Torc or crescent design. Even patination.
£60 - £80

I14-0101
Woad Grinding Set
82mm
Both with suspension loops. Excellent patina.
£300 - £350

I14-0102
Woad Grinding Set
70mm
Both with suspension loops.
£250 - £300

I14-0103
Woad Grinding Set
56mm
Unusual style. Surface a little uneven.

£300 - £350

I14-0104
Woad Grinding Set
45mm
Both parts with suspension loops Even patina.

£150 - £195

I14-0105
Woad Grinding Set
66mm
Smooth, even patination. Traces of enamel.

£200 - £250

I14-0106
Woad Grinding Set
69mm
In the style of two birds heads. Surface a little ragged.

£150 - £200

I14-0107
Woad or Cosmetic
Grinder Set
95mm
Bull's head type. One horn
missing. Surface a little
uneven.
£150 - 200

I14-0201
Woad (Cosmetic)
Grinder
55mm
Pendant pestle from a
grinding set. Even patina.
£25 - £35

I14-0202
Woad (Cosmetic)
Grinder
49mm
Pendant pestle from a
grinding set. Even patina.
£25 - £35

I14-0203
Woad (Cosmetic) Grinder
60mm
Pendant boomerang-shape
pestle from a grinding set.
£25 - £40

I14-0301
Woad (Cosmetic) Grinder
85mm
Boat-shaped base element
of a grinding set, with
suspension loop.
£60 - £80

I14-0302
Woad (Cosmetic) Grinder
70mm
Duck-like shaped base element of a grinding set, with suspension loop.

£60 - £80

I14-0303
Woad (Cosmetic) Grinder
50mm
Banana-shaped base element of a grinding set, with suspension loop.

£50 - £75

I14-0304
Woad (Cosmetic) Grinder
88mm
Boat-shaped base element of a grinding set, with suspension loop. Incised decoration. Very large. Excellent patina.

£75 - £95

I14-0305
Woad (Cosmetic) Grinder
49mm
Phallus-like base element of a grinding set, with suspension loop. Smooth, even patina.

£35 - £50

I14-0306
Woad (Cosmetic) Grinder
48mm
Boat-shaped base element of a grinding set, with suspension loop.

£30 - £50

I14-0307
Woad Cosmetic (Grinder)
63mm
Surface a little ragged.
Complete.
£80 - £90

I14-0308
Woad or Cosmetic
Grinder
35mm
Unusual triple type.
£70 - £80

I14-0401
Woad (Cosmetic) Grinder
78mm
Bull's head. Large size.
Excellent patina. Undamaged.
£600 - £700

I14-0402
Woad Grinder (Bulls Head)
67mm
Unusual style. Surface a little
flaky.
£90 - £120

I14-0501
Mirror
300mm
Elaborately decorated.
Some damage. Very rare
From £35,000

I14-0601
Razor
75mm
Looped handle.
Even patina.
£60 - £80

I14-0602
Razor
115mm
Decoration along
the handle. Loop on
the end. Surface ragged.
£80 - £120

I15-0101
Terret Ring
80mm
Enamelled. Undamaged.
Very large.
From £4,000

I15-0102
Terret Ring
75mm
Most enamel missing. Flaky
surfaces.
From £1,500

I15-0103
Terret Ring
65mm
Three enamelled 'eyes'
around the perimeter.
Slotted junction bar.
£500 - £600

I15-0104
Terret Ring
60mm
Undamaged. Some decoration.
£150 - £250

I15-0105
Terret Ring
60mm
Three decorative knops.
Complete. Undamaged with
an even patina.
£200 - £275

I15-0106
Terret Ring
50mm
Decorated, surface a little
pitted.
£120 - £180

I15-0107
Terret Ring
60mm
Plain "torque" shape. Ragged
surface.
£60 - £80

I15-0108
Terret Ring
70mm
Three moulded projections.
Shape a little distorted.
£50 - £75

I15-0109
Terret Ring
32mm
Small terrett with pronounced
shoulders.
£60 - £100

I15-0110
Terret Ring
25mm
'Torque' shape. Smooth, even
patina. Small.
£25 - £50

I15-0111
Terret Ring
58mm
Ring on flared mounting base.
£90 - £125

I15-0112
Terret Ring
60mm
Ring on flared mounting
base. Sharp detail.
£100 - £150

I15-0113
Terret Ring
55mm
Unusual style. Nice, even patination.
£80 - £100

I15-0114
Terret Ring
48mm
Undamaged. Some decoration.
£100 - £120

I15-0115
Terret Ring
40mm
In the form of two opposing birds.
£70 - £90

I15-0116
Terret RIng
70mm
Six moulded projections. Torc shape. Even patination. Large.
£200 - £250

I15-0117
Terret Ring
55mm
Three enamelled panels around the perimeter. Torc shape. Surface pitted.
£300 - £350

I15-0118
Terret Ring
68mm
Decorated, lipped type. Torc
style. Even green patination.
£200 - £250

I15-0119
Terret Ring
29mm
Red enamelled triangular cell.
Surface a little pitted.
£30 - £40

I15-0201
Horse Cheek Piece
102mm
Enamelled, dragonesque
shape. Very rare.
From £3,000

I15-0202
Horse Cheek Piece
90mm
A little ragged. Three
panels of enamel. Rare.
£400 - £500

I15-0203
Horse Cheek Piece (Toggle)
45mm
Zig-zag pattern with enamel. Rare.
£350 - £400

I15-0204
Cheek Piece
29mm
Plain, undecorated. Slight pitting to the surface.
£100 - £150

I15-0205
Bridal Bit Terminal
44mm dia
Open-work disjointed horse design. Superb patination. Rare.
£600 - £700

I15-0206
Bridal Bit Terminal
44mm dia
Three dragon heads design. Rare.
£500 - £600

I15-0301
Strap Junction
50mm
Double "eye" motif framed by
two panels of inlaid enamel.
Even patina. Enamel
substantially intact.
From £2,000

I15-0302
Harness Strap Junction
60mm
Two human heads.
Even patination. Rare.
£250 - £350

I15-0303
Strap Junction
45mm
Two joined rings with
mounting bars.
£125 - £175

I15-0304
Strap Junction (Iceni)
40mm
Two opposed crescents with mounting bars.
£150 - £250

I15-0305
Strap Junction
45mm
Two opposed crescents with mounting bars.
£150 - £225

I15-0306
Strap Junction
50mm
Two loops divided by a central body with light, incised decoration. Even patina.
£130 - £160

I15-0307
Strap Junction
75mm
Three ring (lower ring broken) stylised bull's head. Rare.
£250 - £300 (Broken)
£500 - £750 (Intact)

I15-0308
Strap Junction
30mm
Double boss with moulded disjointed horse design on the surfaces. Rare.
£200 - £250

I15-0309
Harness Strap Junction
57mm
Three dimensional horse's head. Smooth, even green patination.
£300 - £400

I15-0310
Strap Junction (Frog)
40mm
Bulbous eyed frog. Even patination. Rare.
£100 - £150

I15-0501
Harness Decoration
38mm
Horse's head. Two copper
rivets. Even patina.
£100 - £150

I99-0101
Linch Pin (From Chariot
Wheel)
125mm
Inlaid with enamel.
£400 - £600 (restored)
From £1,500 (unrestored)

I99-0102
Linch Pin (From Chariot)
150mm
Broken in the centre.
£200 - £300

I99-0103
Linch Pin (Bottom End)
24mm dia
Red enamel in circular cells.
£40 - £50

I99-0201
Gold Ring Money
16mm
Decorated and graduated.
£400 - £500

I99-0202
Ring Money (Gold With
Bronze Core)
13mm
Ragged on the surface.
£100 - £120

ROMAN BRITAIN

The very definition of the word 'history' is 'a record of events'. Until two thousand years ago, there had been no such recording, thus the preceding Ages formed our pre-history. But all was to change when a great Empire set its sights on this small island and eventually propelled us into our historic era. However, in the years 55 to 54 BC Julius Caesar singularly failed to add the name of Britannia to the list of Roman provinces and it was to be nearly another one hundred years before the Roman fighting machine successfully invaded these shores. Meanwhile, British Celts did not live in isolation on this side of the channel whilst the Romans ignored them from the other, for treaties had been made by tribal leaders with Caesar and, sometimes, agreed tributes to Rome were even paid up. Communications between Celtic kings and Roman emperors did not cease. An increasing number of Romano-British finds that can be dated to the hundred years between the Julian and Claudian invasions show us that trade between the Empire over the water and the tribes over here must have flourished.

But Rome was not content with these tenuous links and the Claudian invasion of AD 43 heralded four hundred years of Roman subjugation of most of this mainland by sword or sociability. Nearly one half of a millennium of occupation and settlement by a highly civilised and consistent society has, to state the obvious, laid down beneath our soil a vast residue of their life and times and Roman finds continue to be prolific.

In common with previous societies, the Roman layer of soil beneath our feet yields horse trappings, jewellery, weapons, tools, fish-hooks and clothes-fasteners. However, the very nature of the Roman lifestyle, whereby no opportunity was missed to add to the comfort, pleasure and luxury of life, served to expand the list of artefacts displayed in our museums and collected avidly today. For example, municipal baths were an important building in a Roman garrison or town and, with so many people using them in various states of dress and undress, and with so many activities from gambling to business being carried on, it is little wonder that bath house sites have left us with a rich legacy of Romano-British artefacts including strigils (skin-scrapers), tweezers, mirrors, combs, pins and brooches, beads and jewels. Health was as important as hygiene in Roman society so, for the first time, metal surgical instruments form part of the catalogue of artefacts and surgical knives, scalpels, spatulas now turn up.

Whilst prehistoric riches were consigned to secret burial, the principal of lock and key to secure possessions was imported to Britain by the Romans, much to the gratification of modern day key collectors. As education and writing are introduced to our previous illiterate ancestors so the implements thereof become collectors' items today in the shape of iron or bronze styli, used to incise writing on wax. Although the Roman method of eating favoured fingers and knives (but no forks), we now see the first appearance of silver spoons. And the Romans were nothing if not ingenious. As you search for your car keys behind the sofa, think of the Roman who literally wore his key ring on his finger. When your colleague "borrows" your pen and you cannot write down the telephone message, think of the Roman who wore his stylus suspended on a leather thong around his neck. And when the Managing Director cannot locate the Company seal, think of the Roman Governor and his seal-ring secured firmly on his finger. Be you finder, collector or just admirer of ancient artefacts, you have much for which to be grateful to the Romans.

As artefacts from the Roman period are relatively common and readily available, for an item to be valuable it has to be rare or unusual.

R04-0101
Knife Handle (Dog)
55mm
Running dog. Even, dark patina.
£100 - £150

R04-0102
Knife Handle (Panther)
60mm
Scarcer type depicting a panther.
£75 - £125

R04-0103
Folding Knife (Hare & Hound)
65mm
Smooth, even patina. Most of the blade remaining.
£125 - £150

R04-0104
Folding Knife (Hare & Hound)
69mm
Complete with most of the iron blade remaining.
£125 - £150

R04-0105
Folding Knife (Hare & Hound)
68mm
Even patina. Crude style. Blade missing.
£80 - £100

R04-0106
Knife Handle
90mm
Two wrestlers. Superb
patina and rare type.
£1,500 - £2,000

R04-0107
Knife Handle
70mm
Smooth, even patina.
Unusual style.
£100 - £150

R04-0108
Knife Handle
55mm
Surface a little ragged.
Shows signs of wear.
£50 - £80

R04-0109
Knife Handle
78mm
Red and blue enamel
cells. Known type.
£70 - £90

R04-0110
Knife Handle (Hand)
60mm
Even patination. Traces of tinning on the surface. Rare type.
£150 - £200

R04-0111
Sword Crossguard
110mm
Complete. Smooth, even patination.
£125 - £150

R04-0112
Dagger
185mm
Complete with bronze handle and iron blade. Rare.
£300 - £400

R04-0113
Knife
115mm
Bronze phallic crossguard with iron blade.
£100 - £125

R04-0201
Knife or Dagger Pommel (Phallic)
43mm
Probably from a military knife or dagger.
£30 - £40

R04-0202
Knife Pommel (Horse's
Head)
30mm
Fine detail. Even patina.
£150 - £180

R04-0203
Dagger Pommel
35mm
In the form of an eagle's head
holding a seed or nut in its
beak. A little ragged at the
base.
£80 - £100

R04-0204
Sword Pommel
50mm
Eagle's head with light green
patina. Decorated with incised
lines. Undamaged.
£125 - £150

R04-0205
Dagger Pommel
43mm
Good detail. Eagle with a
seed in its beak.
£150 - £200

R04-0206
Knife Pommel (Cupid)
40mm
Cupid picking a thorn from
his foot. Even patination.
£150 - £200

R04-0207
Knife or Dagger
Pommel (Phallic)
40mm
Hand at one end, phallus at
the other.
£40 - £50

R04-0501
Scabbard Chape
62mm
Large with smooth, even green
patination.
£70 - £90

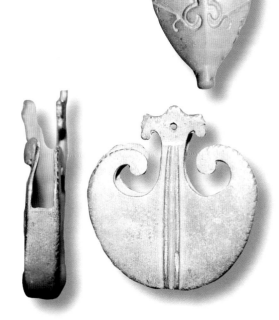

R04-0502
Scabbard Chape
70mm
Large sword scabbard
chape. Good even
patination.
£100 - £150

R06-0101
Pin (Bronze)
100mm
Decorated terminal.
Smooth, even surface.
£30 - £40

R06-0102
Pin (Bronze)
83mm
Ring and dot decorated
hexagonal head.
Surface flaking in places.
£15 - £25

R06-0103
Pin (Bronze)
70mm
Hexagonal head. Smooth,
even patination.
£20 - £30

R06-0104
Bronze Pin (Bird)
115mm
Bird terminal. Decoration
below. Smooth patination.
£40 - £50

R07-0101
Brooch (Bow)
40mm
Unusual style. Wishbone
shape. Pin intact. Even patina.
£70 - £80

R07-0102
Brooch (Bow)
45mm
Pin intact. Even patina.
£30 - £40

R07-0103
Brooch (Bow)
45mm
Pin intact. Even patina.
£35 - £45

R07-0104
Bow Brooch
40mm
Pin intact. Even patina.
£25 - £30

R07-0105
Bow Brooch
45mm
Pin intact. Even patina.
£35 - £45

R07-0106
Bow (Saw) Brooch
45mm
Pin intact. Even patina.
£30 - £40

R07-0107
Bow & Fantail Brooch
38mm
Unusual style. Pin intact.
Even patina.
£100 - £125

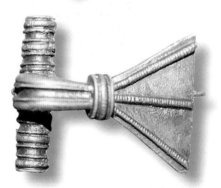

R07-0108
Aesica Brooch (Bow)
48mm
Pin missing. Inlaid panels of
red enamel. Even patina.
£30 - £45

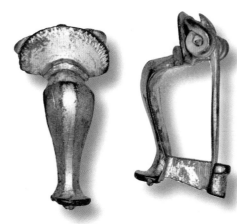

R07-0109
Knee Brooch (Bronze Gilded)
35mm
Complete and undamaged knee brooch. Light decoration to edge of head. Heavily gilded.
£125 - £150

R07-0110
Brooch (Trumpet) Bow
50mm
Pin intact. Some of the enamel remaining.
£50 - £60

R07-0111
Brooch (Bow)
40mm
Even patina. Unusual wishbone style. Pin missing. Suspension loop broken.
£15 - £20

R07-0112
Bow Brooch (Winged)
35mm
Red and blue enamel.
Complete with pin.
£90 - £125

R07-0113
Bow & Fantail Brooch
40mm
Red inlaid enamel. Complete
with pin.
£70 - £90

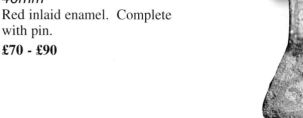

R07-0114
Brooch (Resica Type)
30mm
Smooth, even patination.
Complete with pin.
£60 - £80

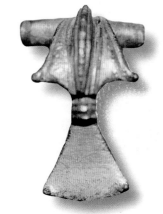

R07-0115
Bow Brooch
30mm
Unusual moulded type.
Smooth, even patination.
No pin.
£40 - £50

R07-0116
Brooch
38mm
Surface a little ragged. No pin.
£30 - £40

R07-0117
Bow Brooch (Headstud)
36mm
Red and blue enamel with
original pin.
£60 - £70

R07-0118
Bow Brooch
37mm
Plain type. Even patination,
with pin.
£15 - £20

R07-0119
Bow Brooch (Silver)
66mm
Unusual type. With pin.
£150 - £180

R07-0120
Bow Brooch
48mm
Smooth patina. No pin.
£5 - £10

R07-0121
Bow Brooch
50mm
Smooth patina. No pin.
£5 - £10

R07-0122
Brooch (Trumpet Type)
45mm
Unusual zoomorphic type.
Good, even surface, with
pin.
£50 - £75

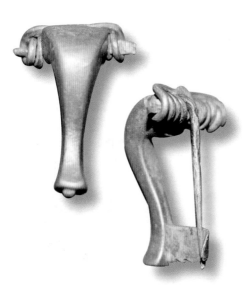

R07-0123
Knee Brooch (Silver)
40mm
Plain type. Complete.
£100 - £125

R07-0124
Knee Brooch
(Enamelled)
34mm
Blue enamelled cells.
Traces of tinning.
Complete with pin.
£30 - £40

R07-0125
Bow Brooch (Enamelled)
58mm
Red and blue enamelled cells.
Complete. Even surfaces.
£150 - £200

R07-0126
Bow Brooch
63mm
Blue enamelled cells. With
pin.
£80 - £100

R07-0127
Bow Brooch
51mm
Trumpet type. Smooth, even
patination. With pin.
£80 - £100

R07-0128
Brooch (Trumpet)
Enamelled
66mm
Blue and yellow enamelled
cells. With pin.
£100 - £125

R07-0129
Bow Brooch
43mm
Traces of red enamel. Silvered
surface. With pin.
£100 - £125

R07-0201
Plate Brooch
30mm
Pin missing. Lunette shape
with inlaid panels of red and
green enamel.
£80 - £100

R07-0202
Plate (Chatelaine) Brooch
115mm
Chatelaine brooch complete with the implements attached. Richly decorated in blue and yellow enamel. Pin intact. Rare.

From £1,250

R07-0203
Plate (Chatelaine) Brooch
50mm
Umbonate type with five rounded lugs. Yellow and brown enamel. Pin intact.

£250 - £350

R07-0204
Plate (Axe) Brooch
30mm
Decorated with blue and brown enamel. Faint traces of silvering. Pin intact.

£125 - £150

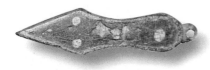

R07-0205
Plate (Sandal) Brooch
42mm
Pin and catchplate intact. Blue and yellow enamel. Slight damage.
£90 - £125

R07-0206
Plate (Sandal) Brooch
42mm
Pin and catchplate intact. Red, blue and yellow enamel. Slightly damaged.
£80 - £100

R07-0207
Plate (Sandal) Brooch
40mm
Pin intact. Most enamel remaining.
£125 - £150

R07-0208
Plate Dolphin Brooch
30mm
Pin intact. Circular central plate with two dolphins either side.
£80 - £120

R07-0209
Plate Brooch
42mm
Pin intact. Unusual style.
Red and blue enamel.
£100 - £150

R07-0210
Plate Brooch (Enamelled)
45mm
Alternating blue and white
enamelled cells. Smooth, even
patination. With pin.
£250 - £300

R07-0211
Plate Brooch
32mm dia
Alternating red and blue
enamelled cells. With pin.
£150 - £175

R07-0212
Plate Brooch (Axe)
30mm
Traces of red enamel. With pin.
£90 - £120

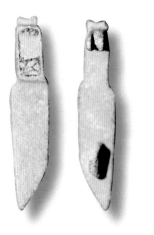

R07-0213
Plate (Knife) Brooch
37mm
Rare type. Traces of red enamel. No pin.
£70 - £90

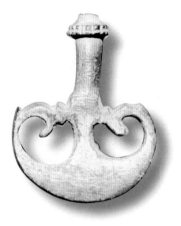

R07-0214
Brooch (Axehead)
30mm
Pelta shape. With pin.
£50 - £70

R07-0215
Plate Brooch
34mm
Three serpents, spiralling. No pin.
£50 - £60

R07-0216
Plate Brooch
35mm
Surface a little uneven. With pin.
£30 - £40

R07-0217
Plate Brooch (Lozenge)
39mm
Even patination. Green glass stone set in the centre. With pin.
£80 - £100

R07-0218
Plate Brooch (Equal Ended)
55mm
Traces of blue enamel. Surface a little patchy. With pin.
£60 - £70

R07-0219
Plate Brooch
40mm
Orange, white and blue
enamelled cells. With pin.
£80 - £100

R07-0220
Plate Brooch
44mm
Blue and orange enamel.
Surface a little ragged.
With pin.
£60 - £70

R07-0221
Plate Brooch
45mm
Enamelled. Surfaces a little
rough. With pin.
£80 - £90

R07-0222
Plate Brooch
34mm
Star shape with blue and white
enamel. Rough surface.
With pin.
£50 - £60

R07-0223
Plate Brooch
48mm
Fully enamelled. Lozenge
shape. With pin.
£120 - £150

R07-0301
Umbonate Brooch
35mm
Pin intact. Inlaid with red and
yellow enamel.
£75 - £100

R07-0302
Umbonate Brooch
37mm
Triangular cells containing
enamel. Tinning on surface.
Pin intact. Even patina.
£100 - £125

R07-0303
Umbonate Brooch
42mm
Unusual style. Eight petals
around the centre. Pin intact.
Excellent patina.
£125 - £150

R07-0304
Brooch (Glass Boss)
Umbonate
35mm
Gilded with black glass stone
set in the centre. Pin missing.
£80 - £100

R07-0305
Brooch (Glass Boss)
Umbonate
38mm
Gilded with black glass stone
set in the centre. Pin intact.
£125 - £150

R07-0306
Brooch (Glass Spiral)
Umbonate
30mm dia
Gilded and set with a colourful stone. With pin.
£275 - £350

R07-0307
Umbonate Brooch
40mm
Heavily enamelled. Safety loop broken. With pin.
£150 - £200

R07-0308
Umbonate Brooch
32mm
Enamelled. Spoked wheel design. With pin.
£100 - £125

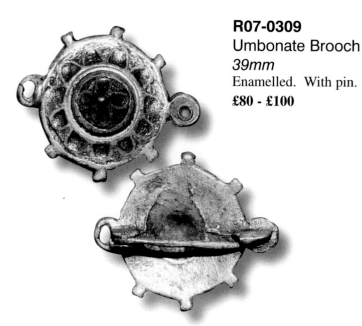

R07-0309
Umbonate Brooch
39mm
Enamelled. With pin.
£80 - £100

R07-0401
Crossbow Brooch
(Gilded)
73mm
Pin intact. Dark green even
patina with much gilding
remaining.
£200 - £250

R07-0402
Crossbow Brooch
85mm
Three onion knops. Decorative
lower section.
Pin missing.
£80 - £100

R07-0403
Silver Crossbow Brooch
(Gilded)
50mm
Pin intact. Original gilding
intact. Rare.
£250 - £350

R07-0404
Silver Crossbow Brooch
72mm
Complete and undamaged.
With pin.
£500 - £600

R07-0405
Brooch (Crossbow Type)
75mm
Good, even patination.
With pin.
£80 - £100

R07-0501
Fish Brooch (Silvered)
41mm
Plate brooch, silvered with
enamel inlay in the eyes. Pin
intact. Rare.
£175 - £200

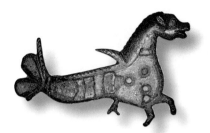

R07-0502
Hippocampus Brooch
50mm
Pin intact. White and orange enamel mainly intact. Head is three dimensional. Rare.
£500 - £600

R07-0503
Hippocampus Brooch
31mm
Pin intact. Blue enamel. Even patina. Rare.
£450 - £550

R07-0504
Plate Brooch
(Beast Looking Back)
30mm
Pin and catchplate intact. Fantastic animal with a rear-facing, crested head. Some blue enamel remaining. Rare.
£150 - £200

R07-0505
Lion Brooch
42mm
Leaping lion. Pin and catch-plate intact. Whole surface tinned. Rare type and large.
£350 - £450

R07-0506
Brooch (Lion)
42mm
Pin intact. Chunky three
dimensional lion in a lying
position. Traces of silvering.
Rare.

£200 - £300

R07-0507
Running Dog Brooch
40mm
Pin intact. Long single cell for
enamel (now lost).
Undamaged example.

£150 - £200

R07-0508
Running Dog Brooch
(Short Tail)
35mm
Pin and catchplate intact.
Central area for enamel (now
lost). Light green patina.

£140 - £175

R07-0509
Plate Brooch (Bird in
Flight)
37mm
Pin intact. Head and neck
three dimensional. Tinning on
the upper surface and red
enamel circles on the wings.
Rare type.

£150 - £200

R07-0510
Bird Brooch
40mm
Pin missing. Bird in flight.
Cells for enamel on wings and
tail. Even patina.
£80 - £100

R07-0511
Duck Brooch (Enamelled)
38mm
Pin intact. Most enamel
remaining. Patina a little
patchy.
£125 - £150

R07-0512
Chicken Brooch
36mm
Pin intact. Inlaid with panels
of red and blue enamel.
£150 - £200

R07-0513
Eagle & Hare Brooch
34mm
Pin missing. Eagle tearing at a
hare. Good condition.
£180 - £220

R07-0514
Hare & Young Brooch
22mm
Pin missing. Decorated with two inlaid enamel hares (only traces of enamel remain).
£80 - £120

R07-0515
Hare Brooch
35mm
Pin intact. Scarce variety with turned up nose.
£150 - £200

R07-0516
Horse & Rider Brooch (Enamelled)
40mm
Unusual style. Surfaces a little ragged. Rare.
£150 - £200

R07-0517
Horse & Rider Brooch (Enamelled)
28mm
Pin intact. Blue and red enamel.
£100 - £150

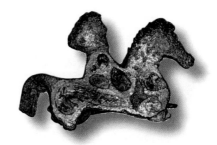

R07-0518
Horse Brooch (Enamelled)
50mm
Pin and catchplate intact. Fully enamelled. Rare type.
£350 - £450

R07-0519
Fly Brooch (Enamelled)
30mm
Fly or insect brooch. Blue and red enamel intact. Pin intact.
£125 - £150

R07-0520
Fly Brooch (Enamelled)
35mm
Enamel intact. Pin in place. Complete example.
£125 - £150

R07-0521
Hare Brooch (Enamelled)
29mm
All the enamel present. Pin intact. Unusual silver border around the body. Rare.
£450 - £500

R07-0522
Hare Brooch
30mm
Some enamel remaining
around the eye. With pin.
£100 - £150

R07-0523
Hare Brooch
22mm
Silver inlay along the body.
With pin.
£100 - £125

R07-0524
Brooch (Hare & Hound)
32mm
Scarce form of brooch.
Surfaces a little ragged.
£80 - £100

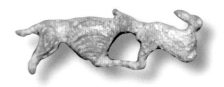

R07-0525
Brooch (Hare & Hound)
35mm
Seated hound tearing at a hare.
No pin.
£60 - £80

R07-0526
Brooch (Stag)
35mm
Decoration along the body.
With pin.
£80 - £100

R07-0527
Brooch (Stag)
40mm
Fully enamelled. Ground
line. No pin but scarce type.
£400 - £450

R07-0528
Brooch (Panther)
45mm
Unusual type with collar
around its neck. Enamel a
little patchy.
£300 - £400

R07-0529
Panther Brooch
(Enamelled)
44mm
Good light green patination.
No pin.
£300 - £400

R07-0530
Brooch (Lion)
40mm
Red and blue enamel cells.
Complete with pin.
£250 - £300

R07-0531
Fly Brooch (Enamelled)
32mm
Unusual type of fly brooch.
Red and blue enamel. With
pin.
£100 - £130

R07-0532
Brooch (Horse & Rider)
27mm
Plain type. With pin.
£70 - £80

R07-0533
Horse & Rider Brooch
(Enamelled)
33mm
Surface a little ragged. Some
enamel remaining. With pin.
£120 - £150

R07-0534
Horse & Rider Brooch
33mm
Traces of enamel. Surface a
little uneven. With pin.
£130 - £160

R07-0535
Horse & Rider Brooch
33mm
Red and blue enamel. Smooth,
even patination. With pin.
£120 - £150

R07-0536
Horse & Rider Brooch
30mm
Traces of enamel. Horse has
very large tail. With pin.
£100 - £130

R07-0537
Horse Brooch
35mm
Nice bold example. Surface a
little uneven. With pin.
£250 - £325

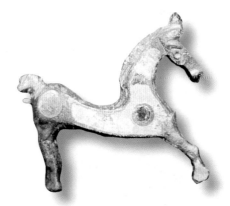

R07-0538
Horse Brooch
35mm
Enamelled cells. Ring and dot
decoration on the neck and
mane.
£250 - £300

R07-0539
Boar Brooch
40mm
Traces of enamel. Surface a
little rough. No pin.
£150 - £200

R07-0540
Boar Brooch
31mm
Red enamel cell. Suspension loop at the rear. No pin.
£150 - £200

R07-0541
Boar Brooch
40mm
Red and blue enamelled cells. Turned up snout and curly tail. No pin.
£400 - £450

R07-0542
Boar Brooch
38mm
Light and dark blue enamelled cells. Turned up snout and curly tail. No pin.
£400 - £450

R07-0543
Brooch (Boar)
42mm
Blue and white enamelled cells. Curly tail. No pin.
£350 - £400

R07-0544
Brooch (Fish)
43mm
Good detail. Enamelled eye. Silvered surface.
£150 - £200

R07-0545
Brooch (Frog)
34mm
Surface a little ragged.
Enamelled cells.
Glass beads in eyes. With pin.
£300 - £400

R07-0546
Brooch (Frog)
40mm
Enamelled cells. One rear
back leg broken. No pin.
£250 - £300

R07-0547
Sea Serpant Brooch
60mm
Eel like sea monster. Enamel
along the body. Scarce type.
No pin.
£350 - £400

R07-0548
Hippocampus Brooch
53mm
Red and blue enamel mainly
intact. Three dimensional
head. No pin.
£450 - £500

R07-0549
Hippocampus Brooch
50mm
Enamelled cells mainly intact.
Smooth, even patination.
No pin.
£475 - £550

R07-0550
Two Headed Monster Brooch
42mm
Most enamel remaining. Surface a little uneven. No pin.
£300 - £350

R07-0551
Swan Brooch (Enamelled)
30mm
Very rare type of brooch in the form of a swan. Red and blue enamel. No pin.
£450 - £550

R07-0552
Peacock Brooch
32mm
Complete with pin. Surface a little pitted.
£140 - £170

R07-0553
Peacock Brooch (Enamelled)
30mm
As previous. No pin and surface heavily pitted.
£100 - £120

R07-0554
Duck Brooch
32mm
Complete with pin. Patina a little patchy. Single colour enamel.

£120 - £170

R07-0555
Duck Brooch (Enamelled)
31mm
Complete with pin. Beak broken. Surface a little ragged.

£80 - £100

R07-0556
Bird Brooch
40mm
Bird in flight. Pin missing. Enamelled cells.

£90 - £100

R07-0557
Bird Brooch
30mm
Plain type. Incised line decoration. With pin.

£70 - £80

R07-0558
Bird Brooch
20mm
Small size. With pin.
£50 - £60

R07-0559
Bird Brooch
28mm
Surface a little ragged.
Pin missing.
£30 - £40

R07-0601
Disc Brooch
(Enamelled)
31mm dia
Pin intact. With red enamel
and inlaid with panels of
millefiori style yellow
enamel.
£75 - £90

R07-0602
Disc Brooch (Celtic Cross)
33mm dia
Pin intact. Remains of blue
enamel. Unusual style.
£100 - £130

R07-0603
Disc Brooch (Enamelled)
36mm dia
Undamaged with pin intact.
Inlaid with rings of yellow
enamel and one band of blue
and red millefiori style
decoration.
£200 - £300

R07-0604
Disc brooch
(Fully Enamelled)
39mm
Large size. Fully enamelled.
With pin.
£240 - £280

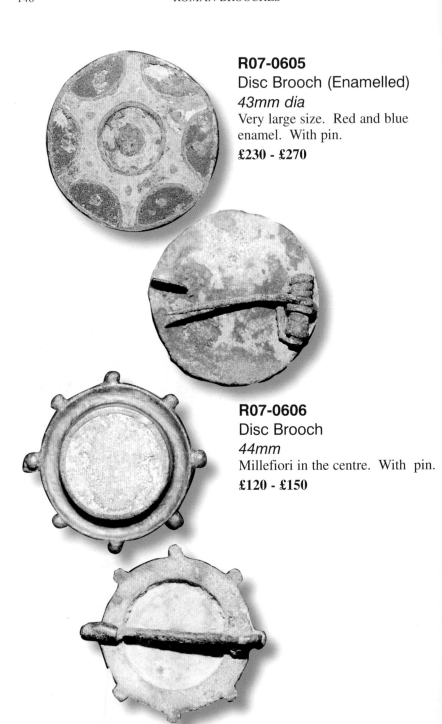

R07-0605
Disc Brooch (Enamelled)
43mm dia
Very large size. Red and blue
enamel. With pin.
£230 - £270

R07-0606
Disc Brooch
44mm
Millefiori in the centre. With pin.
£120 - £150

R07-0607
Disc Brooch (Enamelled)
30mm dia
All enamel remaining. With
pin.
£120 - £150

R07-0608
Disc Brooch (Enamelled)
39mm dia
Large size. Enamel damaged
in places. With pin.
£110 - £140

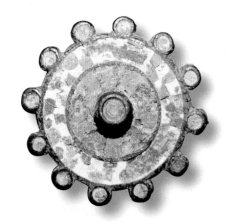

R07-0609
Disc Brooch (Enamelled)
41mm
Large size. Virtually fully
enamelled. With pin.
£140 - £180

R07-0610
Disc Brooch (Enamelled)
30mm dia
Enamel a little fuzzy. With pin.
£80 - £100

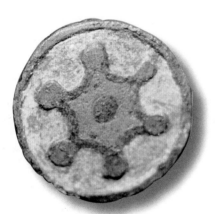

R07-0611
Disc Brooch (Enamelled)
23mm dia
Surface a little ragged. With pin.
£70 - £80

R07-0612
Disc Brooch (Enamelled)
27mm dia
Surface a little rough. Stone missing from centre. With pin.
£70 - £80

R07-0613
Disc Brooch (Enamelled)
34mm dia
Six pointed star design within
a circle. With pin.
£150 - £180

R07-0614
Brooch (Disc) Gilded
23mm dia
Wheel design. Traces of
gilding.
£50 - £60

R07-0615
Disc Brooch (Openwork)
35mm dia
Even patina. With pin.
£50 - £70

R07-0701
Penannular Brooch
(Bronze)
30mm
Surface a little pitted. Pin
intact. Torque shape.
£35 - £45

R07-0702
Penannular Brooch
22mm
Smooth, even patina. Pin
intact. Incised decoration.
Small size.
£30 - £40

R07-0703
Penannular Brooch
25mm dia
Silver. Small break at the
end of the pin.
£80 - £100

R08-0101
Pendant (Phallic)
31mm
Typical style. Worn as a fertility charm.
£35 - £45

R08-0102
Pendant (Phallic)
35mm
Bronze phallus pendant of typical form. Often associated with the military. Dark patina.
£60 - £70

R08-0103
Pendant (Phallic)
32mm
Bronze phallic pendant of unusual form. Even patina.
£60 - £70

R08-0104
Pendant (Phallic)
31mm
Bronze phallic pendant of usual form. Even patina.
£60 - £70

R08-0105
Pendant (Phallic)
35mm
Bronze phallic pendant.
A little pitted on the surface.
Slim style.
£50 - £60

R08-0106
Pendant (Phallic)
43mm
Large size. Even patina.
£70 - £80

R08-0107
Pendant
40mm
Flat form. Smooth,
even patina.
£70 - £80

R08-0108
Pendant (Phallus)
49mm
Surface a little pitted.
£100 - £125

R08-0109
Pendant (Phallic)
40mm
Patina a little uneven. Triple phallus.
£110 - £140

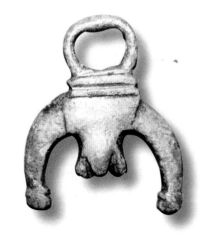

R08-0110
Pendant (Phallic)
50mm
Large size. Surface a little uneven.
£80 - £90

R08-0111
Pendant (Phallic)
34mm
Basic style. Even patina.
£70 - £80

R08-0112
Pendant
(Winged Phallus) Silver
27mm
Rare silver winged phallus.
Good detail.
£350 - £400

R08-0201
Pendant (Military)
96mm
Disc inlaid with silver sheet,
much remaining.
Pendant portion depicts four
dolphins around a typical
military design.
£250 - £350

R08-0202
Pendant (Military)
65mm
Inlaid numeral 'V' perhaps
denoting the fifth legion.
£75 - £100

R08-0203
Pendant (Military)
75mm
Suspension boss with pendant
of stylised phallic form.
Probably a military belt fitting.
£60 - £80

R08-0301
Pendant (Axehead)
17mm
In the style of a Bronze Age
socketed axe. Surface a little
ragged.
£20 - £25

R08-0302
Pendant
22mm
Crescent shaped pendant.
Traces of silver inlay. Surface
a little rough.
£30 - £40

R08-0303
Pendant (Knife)
43mm
Smooth, even green surface.
Rare knife pendant.
£70 - £90

R08-0304
Pendant (Gold)
19mm
Half round stone set in a decorated border.
£350 - £450

R09-0101
Mount (Crested Helmet)
38mm
Bronze bust in native style.
Even patina.
£75 - £90

R09-0102
Mount (Mars)
44mm
Mars in a Corinthian helmet.
£80 - £100

R09-0103
Mount (Minerva)
35mm
Fine detail. Head of the
goddess Minerva.
Even patina.
£150 - £200

R09-0104
Mount
32mm
Head with elaborate hair
design.
£75 - £125

R09-0105
Mount (Sol Invictus)
37mm
Romano-British bust of Sol
Invictus (the sun god). Even
patina.
£125 - £180

R09-0106
Mount (Sol Invictus)
45mm
Bust of Sol Invictus (the sun
god). Even patina.
£175 - £250

R09-0107
Mount (Sol Invictus)
40mm
Classical style. Dark, even
patina.
£175 - £250

R09-0108
Mount (Cherub)
50mm
Hollow back. Lightly moulded
features. Probably from an
item of furniture.
£100 - £125

R09-0109
Mount (Apollo)
39mm
Well formed features. Dark
tone.
£150 - £200

R09-0110
Mount (Apollo)
42mm
Classical style bust of Apollo.
Very fine detail. Rare.
£250 - £350

R09-0111
Mount (Mother Goddess)
49mm
Bronze mount, probably representing a mother goddess.
Dark green patina.
£150 - £200

R09-0112
Mount (Military-Bacchus)
37mm
Lunette body with the face of a
bearded deity. Ragged patina.
£150 - £200

R09-0113
Mount (Gruesome Face)
32mm
Circular mount with a
gruesome face in the centre.
Patina a little ragged.
£60 - £70

R09-0114
Mount (Mithras)
85mm
Very large. Good detail. Even
patination. Rare.
From £3,000

R09-0115
Mount
50mm
Head of Mercury.
Good detail. Even patination.
£400 - £500

R09-0116
Mount (Horned God)
27mm
Dark patination. Good detail.
£120 - £150

R09-0117
Mount (Silver)
20mm
Horned god in silver.
One horn broken.
£150 - £200

R09-0118
Mount (Celtic Style Head)
37mm
Uneven surface.
Celtic features.
£100 - £140

R09-0119
Mount
50mm
Rough surface. Dark patina.
Some damage.
£120 - £150

R09-0120
Mount
37mm
Probably from a bowl. Celtic
features.
£100 - £150

R09-0121
Mount (Bust of Sol)
38mm
Slight scuff across the face.
Good detail.
£150 - £200

R09-0122
Mount (Cherub)
45mm
Perfect patination. Very
sharp detail. Cherub
squeezing grapes.
£300 - £350

R09-0123
Mount
35mm
Very rough surface.
Detail a little weak.
£80 - £100

R09-0124
Mount (Lead) Female
Head
30mm
Has a cut (made in
antiquity) across its face.
£50 - £60

R09-0125
Mount
85mm
Probably from a bowl or dish.
Even patination.
£300 - £350

R09-0126
Mount
32mm
Bearded face.
£50 - £75

R09-0127
Mount
72mm
Large female bust. Hollow at
the back.
Surface a little rough.
£250 - £300

R09-0201
Mount (Horse Harness)
Military
35mm
Two horses' heads back-to-back. Two rectangular fixing loops on the back.
£100 - £130

R09-0202
Mount
(Forepart of a Horse)
37mm
Equestrian mount probably from a bowl.
£50 - £75

R09-0203
Mount (Hanging Bowl)
32mm
Horse's head mount from a hanging bowl. Patina a little patchy.
£75 - £90

R09-0204
Mount (Ram's Head)
20mm
Ram's head with arched horns.
May have been a pin head.
£35 - £45

R09-0205
Mount (Lion's Head)
30mm
Crude style. Even patina.
£30 - £40

R09-0206
Mount (Lion's Head)
54mm
Good detail. Nice, even green
patination.
£200 - £250

R09-0207
Mount (Horse's Head)
30mm
Patchy surface.
Three dimensional.
£60 - £75

R09-0208
Mount (Ram's Head)
35mm
Patination a little patchy.
Good detail.
£100 - £120

R09-0301
Mount (Enamelled)
26mm
Circular floral design with red,
green and yellow enamel.
£50 - £60

R09-0302
Mount (Enamelled)
23mm
Circular mount, most enamel
remaining.
£50 - £60

R09-0303
Mount (Military)
27mm
Native style. Dark patina.
£30 - £45

R09-0304
Mount (Enamelled)
25mm
Hexagonal shape.
Most enamel remaining.
£50 - £60

R09-0401
Owl Mount
40mm

Mounted on a solid circular base, the owl has two cylindrical legs. Head looking forward and wings folded. Examples of owls found in Britain are very rare. Usually associated with the goddess Minerva.

£450 - £500

R09-0402
Mount (Baby Turtle)
21mm

Traces of silvering and enamel in the eyes.

£25 - £30

R09-0403
Mount (Eagle)
50mm
Spread wings with feathers detailed. Mounted on a stem. Perhaps from a military standard.

£175 - £225

R09-0404
Mount (Sleeping Dog)
35mm
Sleeping dog with a collar around the neck. Integral suspension on the dog's back. Perhaps from a hanging bowl or similar. Even patina.

£150 - £180

R09-0405
Mount (Sleeping Dog)
31mm
Even patina. Slight damage.

£60 - £70

R09-0405(a)
Mount (Sphinx)
30mm
Sphinx (without beard). Fair detail. Surface a little pitted. Rare from this country.
£200 - £250

R09-0406
Mount (Harness) Military
45mm
Typical military style. Good surface and patina.
£40 - £60

R09-0407
Mount (Phallic)
30mm
Two fixing lugs underneath. Undamaged. Even patina.
£50 - £60

R09-0408
Hanging Bowl Mount
(Phallic)
73mm
Complete and undamaged.
Good, even green patina-
tion. Rare.
£450 - £500

R09-0409
Mount (Military) Vine
Leaf
71mm dia
Mounting stud on rear.
Small piece of blue enamel
showing, remainder miss-
ing. Good, even patina.
£160 - £180

R09-0410
Mount (Cheekpiece)
72mm
Smooth, even surface. Large
size. Good patina.
£200 - £250

R09-0411
Mount (Boar)
47mm
Very rough surface. Silvered boar.
£100 - £120

R09-0412
Mount (Bowl)
35mm
Foot from a bowl. Good detail.
£40 - £50

R09-0413
Mount (Sleeping Dog)
38mm
Even green patination.
£70 - £80

R09-0414
Mount (Eagle)
52mm
Good detail. Surface a little
uneven.
£250 - £300

R09-0415
Mount (Eagle)
50mm
Crude style, more like a dodo.
Even patination.
£100 - £150

R09-0416
Mount (Eagle)
50mm
Sad looking. Incised line decoration on the body.
£100 - £120

R09-0417
Mount (Eagle)
43mm
Surface a little flaky. Looks like a pigeon.
£60 - £70

R09-0418
Mount (Harness) Military Phallic
38mm
Good detail. Loop on the back.
£90 - £120

R09-0419
Mount (Phallic) Enamelled
34mm
Most enamel remaining. Good size.
£50 - £60

R09-0420
Mount (Phallic)
26mm
Good detail. Has two fixing holes.
£90 - £100

R10-0101
Ring (Gold)
23mm int dia
Inset with a chalcedony seal stone, engraved with a standing figure with an eagle at his feet. Large wearable size.

From £1,500

R10-0102
Gold Ring
(Clasped Hands)
24mm
Solid construction (15.25 grammes). Bezel depicts clasped hands. Wearable size. Rare.

From £2,000

R10-0103
Ring (Gold)
Eagle on Intaglio
13mm
Orange stone intaglio depicting a
spread eagle. Small size.
£150 - £200

R10-0104
Ring (Gold)
20mm
Solid construction. Original
intaglio with a crack across the
centre. Wearable size.
From £600

R10-0105
Ring (Gold)
Garnet Stone
17mm int dia
Unusual style.
Original stone.
Undamaged.
£300 - £400

R10-0106
Gold Ring
23mm dia
Bezel cracked.
Good size
chunky ring.
£400 - £500

R10-0107
Gold Ring
(Clasped Hands)
31mm dia
Decorated band. Good size.
Rare.
From £3,000

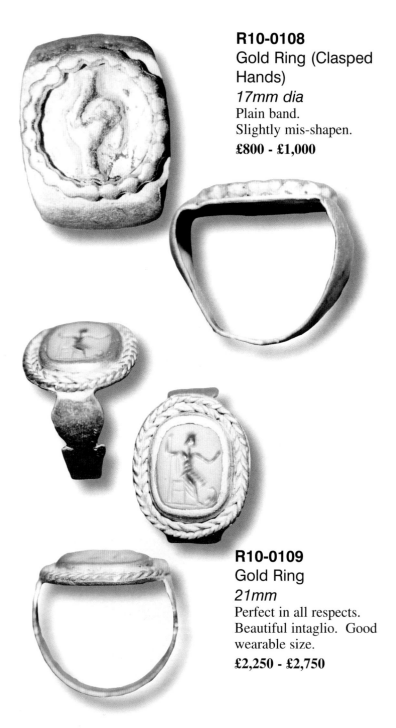

R10-0108
Gold Ring (Clasped Hands)
17mm dia
Plain band.
Slightly mis-shapen.
£800 - £1,000

R10-0109
Gold Ring
21mm
Perfect in all respects.
Beautiful intaglio. Good wearable size.
£2,250 - £2,750

R10-0110
Gold Ring
20mm
Small size.
Open-work band.
Original intaglio.
£700 - £900

R10-0111
Gold Ring
17mm
Small size.
Original stone set.
£600 - £700

R10-0112
Gold Ring (Palm Leaf)
13mm
Probably a child's ring.
Engraved palm leaf design on bezel.
£125 - £175

R10-0201
Ring (Silver)
18mm int dia
Blue intaglio engraved with a
bird. Hunched shoulders.
Good condition.
£100 - £150

R10-0202
Ring (Silver) Spes
15mm int dia
Dark red coloured intaglio
engraved with a female figure.
Small size.
£120 - £140

R10-0203
Silver Finger Ring
(Mercury)
21mm dia
Bezel is a silver insert depicting Mercury. Wearable size.
£300 - £350

R10-0204
Ring (Silver)
20mm int dia
Original black glass intaglio
engraved with a standing
figure.
£150 - £175

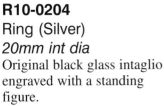

R10-0205
Silver Finger Ring
(Ceres)
24mm dia
Red stone intaglio depicting
Ceres. Good quality
engraving.
£200 - £250

R10-0206
Silver Finger Ring
16mm dia
Chunky but small size with
cornelian intaglio engraved
with the figure of Ceres.
£200 - £250

R10-0207
Silver Ring (Mars Intaglio)
18mm dia
Red cornelian intaglio
engraved with the figure of
Mars. Wearable size.

£250 - £300

R10-0208
Silver Finger Ring
(Minerva)
16mm dia
Red glass intaglio depicting
Roma or Minerva. Small size.

£120 - £150

R10-0209
Silver Finger Ring (Eagle)
Military
20mm dia
Traces of gilding. Legionary
eagle on bezel.
£80 - £125

R10-0210
Silver Finger Ring
19mm dia
Flared shoulders. Light
engraved design on bezel and
on shoulders.
£80 - £125

R10-0211
Ring Silver (Concordia)
17mm int dia
Red glass intaglio depicting
Concordia. Wearable size.
£125 - £150

R10-0212
Ring (Silver)
21mm int dia
In the form of a coiled snake.
Wearable size.
£150 - £180

R10-0213
Ring (Silver)
20mm dia
Decorated band engraved
intaglio
£225 - £300

R10-0214
Silver Ring
19mm
Glass intaglio with Venus
engraved.
£150 - £200

R10-0215
Silver Ring
19mm int dia
Chunky ring. Plain stone.
£150 - £175

R10-0216
Silver Ring
19mm
Crescent moon and stars
engraved on the intaglio
(Hadrian period).
£200 - £250

R10-0217
Silver Ring (Venus)
18mm
Venus engraved on the intaglio.
£200 - £250

R10-0218
Silver Finger Ring
20mm
Patchy colour.
A little misshapen.
£140 - £175

R10-0219
Silver Ring
18mm
Military shape. Ears of corn engraved on the intaglio.

£150 - £180

R10-0220
Silver Ring (Snake)
20mm
Surface a little ragged. Twin serpent heads.

£175 - £200

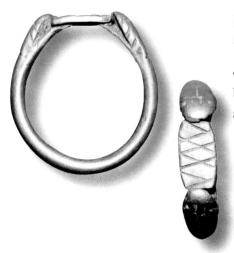

R10-0221
Silver Finger Ring
18mm
Two serpents holding a panel between their mouths.
£125 - £150

R10-0222
Silver Ring (Inscription)
22mm dia
Wearable ring with inscription.
£220 - £250

R10-0223
Silver Ring
26mm
Chunky and large military ring.
Plain bezel.
£125 - £150

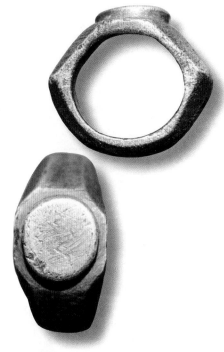

R10-0301
Bronze Ring
(With Inscription)
22mm dia
Inscription on Bezel "CVTVX-
CT". Dark, even patina.
Scarce.
£75 - £100

R10-0302
Bronze Finger Ring
21mm dia
Facetted bezel inset with a
blue-green glass intaglio,
engraved
with a standing figure.
£75 - £100

R10-0303
Bronze Finger Ring
18mm dia
Military style.
Bezel an integral part of ring.
Wearable size.
£35 - £50

R10-0304
Bronze Finger Ring
19mm dia
Unusual bronze ring with
engraved bezel.
Good patination.
£80 - £100

R10-0401
Earring (Gold)
With Garnet
18mm dia
Set with a fine deep red garnet.
Decorative border and plain
suspension loop.
£450 - £550

R11-0101
Statuette (Mars)
85mm
Mars wearing full armour and holding his cloak. Spear and shield missing. Very fine even green patina. Undamaged.
from £1,200

R11-0102
Statuette (Mercury)
104mm
Superb detail. Feet missing. Good dark matt surface.
£750 - £850

R11-0103
Statuette (Mercury)
52mm
Mercury holding a caduceus.
Feet missing. Well Modelled.
Dark patina.
£150 - £190

R11-0104
Statuette (Mercury)
58mm
Good detail. Mercury holding
a purse and wearing a winged
cap. Traces of tinning on the
surface. Right leg severed in
antiquity, possibly for votive
reasons.
£200 - £295

R11-0105
Statuette (Cupid)
70mm
Right leg broken. Good, even
surface.
£350 - £450

R11-0106
Statuette
(Drunk Hercules)
85mm
Hercules holding a drinking
vessel in his right hand and a
club in his left. He has a
lion's skin draped over his left
arm.
Good patina and condition.
£700 - £900

R11-0107
Statuette (Hercules)
75mm
In native Celtic style. Fluid
lines to the body. Dark even
patina. Right leg broken.
£250 - £300

R11-0108
Venus Statue
55mm
Even patina. Feet broken
away.
£200 - £300

R11-0109
Naked Youth Statue
102mm
Good detail. Even patina.
Complete and undamaged.
£500 - £600

R11-0110
Statuette (Female
Holding Purse)
92mm
Good even and smooth surface.
Attractive patination.
£600 - £700

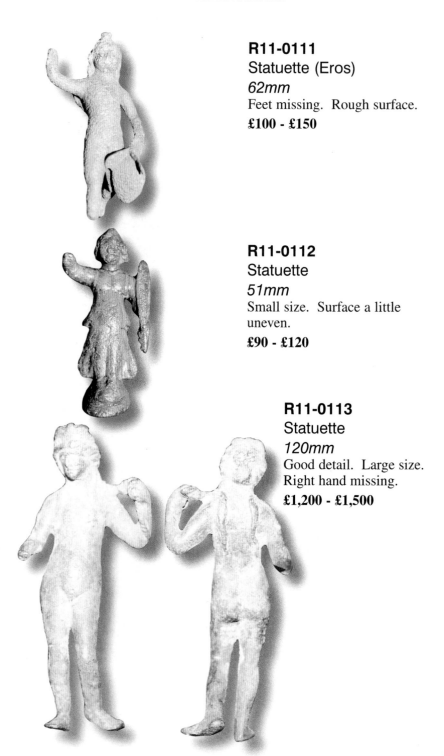

R11-0111
Statuette (Eros)
62mm
Feet missing. Rough surface.
£100 - £150

R11-0112
Statuette
51mm
Small size. Surface a little
uneven.
£90 - £120

R11-0113
Statuette
120mm
Good detail. Large size.
Right hand missing.
£1,200 - £1,500

R11-0114
Statuette
98mm
Good size. Surface a little rough.
£500 - £600

R11-0115
Statuette
75mm
Surface a little rough.
£250 - £300

R11-0116
Statuette (Cupid)
70mm
Rare to be holding a torch. One wing missing on back.
£350 - £400

R11-0117
Statue (Ass. Dionysus)
68mm
Unusual statuette with silver sheet applied.
£250 - £300

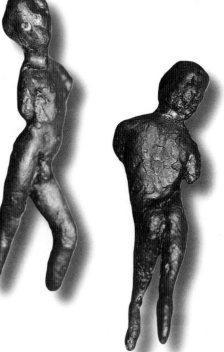

R11-0118
Statue (Apollo)
108mm
Silver eyes. Surface very ragged.
£400 - £450

R11-0119
Statuette (Jupiter)
88mm
Good detail. Smooth, even
surface. Holding thunderbolt.
£800 - £1,000

R11-0120
Naked Male Statue
78mm
Rich green patination. Quiver
for arrows on his back.
£450 - £500

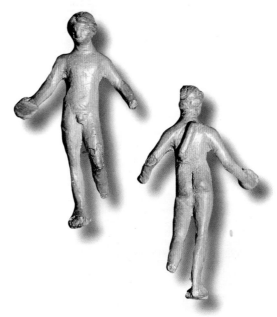

R11-0121
Statue
55mm
Rare statue of Priapus.
£700 - £750

R11-0201
Statuette (Goat)
42mm
Good detail. Even patina.
One horn missing from top of head.
£350 - £400

R11-0202
Mouse (With Bread)
27mm
Patina a little ragged. Small size.
£130 - £175

R11-0203
Statuette (Eagle)
55mm
Good, even surface.
Has animal at its feet.
£300 - £350

R12-0201
Buckle (Two Dolphins)
32mm
Frame in the form of two dolphin heads with a ball held in their mouths. Pin missing.
£40 - £50

R12-0202
Buckle (Gilded)
34mm
Roman military buckle.
Heavily gilded.
£50 - £75

R12-0203
Buckle (With Plate)
78mm
Enamelled plate.
Open-work buckle.
£100 - £150

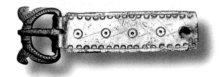

R12-0204
Buckle (With Plate)
64mm
Ring and dot decoration.
Smooth, even
patination.
£70 - £90

R12-0205
Buckle (With Plate)
Military
45mm
Ring and dot decoration.
Surface a little patchy.
£60 - £80

R12-0301
Strap End (Amphora Type)
53mm
Incised decoration with securing rivets intact.

£40 - £50

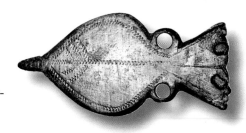

R12-0401
Belt Fitting (Military)
133mm long
Disc with attachment plates. Even patina.

£175 - £250

R13-0101
Clothes Fastener
30mm
Decorative and brightly enamelled, most of which remains.

£120 - £150

R14-0101
Mirror Surround (With Inscription)
56x52mm
Lead mirror surround. Inscription reads "GENTILIUS MELAUSUS". Rare item.

£100 - £150

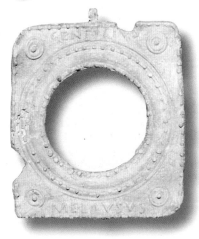

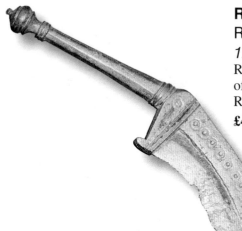

R14-0201
Razor (Iron Blade) Bronze
120mm
Ring and dot decoration. Most of the iron blade remaining. Rare.

£400 - £500

R16-0101
Seal Box (Complete)
32mm
Traces of enamel. Lid and base do not open.

£80 - £95

R16-0102
Seal Box (With Lid)
27mm
Most of the enamel remaining. Lid and base do not open.

£85 - £95

R16-0103
Seal Box (Complete)
45mm
Damaged on the base. Traces
of enamel. Does not open.
£40 - £50

R16-0104
Seal Box
(Complete)
33mm
Enamel inlay on the lid.
In working order.
Even patina.
£85 - £95

R16-0105
Seal Box (With Lid)
31mm
Enamel inlay on the lid.
Does not open.
Even patina.
£70 - £80

R16-0106
Seal Box
(Complete)
31mm
Enamel inlay on the
lid which does not
open. Even patina.
£80 - £100

R16-0107
Seal Box (Enamelled)
32mm
Enamel inlay on the lid which does not open. Patina a little uneven.

£70 - £80

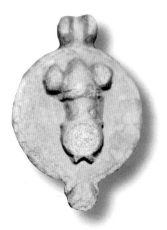

R16-0108
Seal Box (Complete)
26mm
Enamelled phallus on the lid which does not open.
Scarce type.

£80 - £100

R16-0109
Seal Box
27mm
Beast looking rearwards on the lid which does not open.

£80 - £100

R16-0110
Seal Box (Silver)
37mm
Very rare seal box in silver.
Probably military.
From £500

R16-0201
Seal Box Lid
30mm
In Celtic style. Lid is
missing its base. Most
enamel present.
£40 - £50

R16-0202
Seal Box Lid
20mm
Celtic style.
Lid missing its base.
Most enamel remaining.
£40 - £50

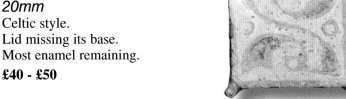

R17-0101
Ring Key
19mm
Hollow shank and offset
wards.
£35 - £40

R17-0102
Ring Key
18mm
Combined finger ring and key.
£35 - £45

R17-0103
Ring Key
25mm
Combined finger ring and key.
£30 - £45

R17-0104
Ring Key
24mm
Combined finger ring and key.
£20 - £25

R17-0105
Ring Key
28mm
Combined finger ring and key.
Even patina.
£35 - £50

R17-0106
Ring Key
35mm
Combined finger ring and key.
Detailed wards with linear
decoration. Good example.
£45 - £65

R17-0107
Ring Key (Unusual
Wards)
34mm
Round body with offset wards
of ten pins. Even patina.
Unusual example.
£50 - £60

R17-0108
Ring Key
31mm
Combined finger ring and key.
Fairly plain. Even patina.
£25 - £35

R17-0109
Key (Bronze)
38mm
Offset wards. Perfect and
undamaged.
Oustanding patina.
£70 - £80

R17-0110
Keys (Bronze)
longest 58mm
Group of three keys illustrating the three main varieties. All in good condition.

From £25 each

R17-0201
Keys (Iron)
longest 90mm
Group of four latch lifter keys made of iron.

From £20 each

R17-0202
Key (Bronze) With Shank
44mm
Typical shank and offset wards. Even patina.

£50 - £60

R17-0203
Key With Shank
44mm
Hexagonal shank. Sharp detail. Even green patina.

£50 - £60

R17-0204
Key With Shank
41mm
Typical shank and offset wards. Even patina.
£50 - £60

R17-0205
Key With Shank
65mm
Big chunky handle, with light green decoration. Even green patina.
£50 - £65

R17-0206
Key With Shank
64mm
Long, solid handle decorated with simple incised decoration. Even patina. Perfect condition.
£60 - £80

R17-0207
Key (Bronze) Lunette Top
34mm
Fine detail. Even patina.
£60 - £70

R17-0208
Key (Bronze)
40mm
Typical form with offset wards.
Surface a little ragged.
£20 - £25

R17-0209
Key (Unusual Style)
Military?
75mm
Pelta shape handle. Very
unusual style for a bronze key.
Rare.
£125 - £175

R17-0210
Key (Bronze)
73mm
Typical form but unusual in
having a bronze rather than an
iron shank.
£40 - £60

R17-0211
Key (Bronze)
30mm
Even patina. Unusual style.
£35 - £40

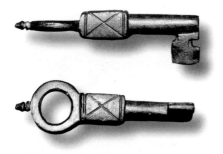

R17-0212
Key (Bronze)
With Shank
57mm
Decorated.
Smooth, even patination.
£70 - £80

R17-0213
Key (Bronze)
83mm
Large and chunky. Patina
flaking in places.
£120 - £150

R17-0301
Key & Lock Group
85mm (key)
Key has bronze handle and
iron shank. Iron in good
condition and stable. Two
bronze lock bolts.
£70 - £90

R17-0401
Key Handle
75mm
Bronze handle with part of
iron shank remaining.
Typical form.
£35 - £50

R17-0402
Key Handle
70mm
Bronze handle with fraction
of iron shank remaining.
£35 - £50

R17-0403
Key Handle
(Lion & Celt)
120mm
Patina a little patchy.
Good detail. Rare.
From £700

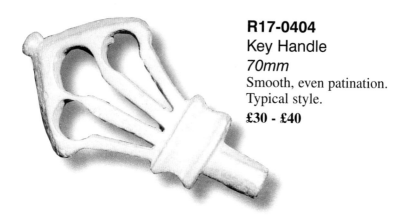

R17-0404
Key Handle
70mm
Smooth, even patination.
Typical style.
£30 - £40

R18-0101
Steelyard Set
115mm
Balance arm with two hooks
and two scale pans. Steelyard
weight missing.
£120 - £150

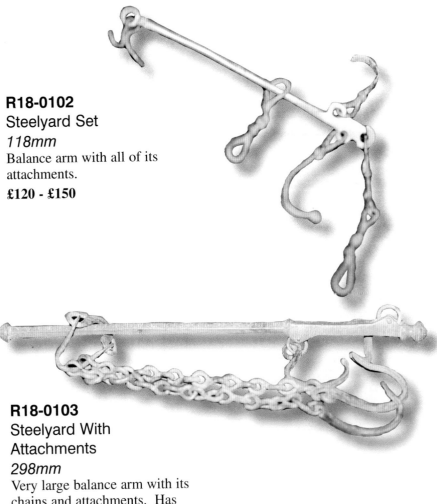

R18-0102
Steelyard Set
118mm
Balance arm with all of its
attachments.
£120 - £150

R18-0103
Steelyard With
Attachments
298mm
Very large balance arm with its
chains and attachments. Has
scale markings along its
length.
£300 - £400

R18-0104
Steelyard
89mm
Balance arm with one hook.
£80 - £100

R18-0201
Steelyard Weight
31mm
Crude style head, most features
worn away. Patina a little
ragged.
£60 - £80

R18-0202
Steelyard Weight
30mm
Crude style female head.
Weak detail. Even patina.
£70 - £90

R18-0203
Steelyard Weight
55mm
Youthful bust with good detail.
Fine definition of face and hair.
£200 - £250

R18-0204
Steelyard Weight
(Cockerel)
35mm
Good detail. Complete and
undamaged. Even patina.
£70 - £90

R18-0205
Steelyard Weight
60mm
Good detail. With its
suspension chain.
£800 - £900

R18-0206
Steelyard Weight
90mm
Ring and dot decoration.
£60 - £70

R19-0101
Stylus (With Enamel)
Pendant
51mm
Pendant with stylus point,
inlaid with dots of red enamel.
Rare.
£100 - £125

R19-0102
Stylus (Bronze)
53mm
Pendant with stylus point.
Decorated along the shank.
Even patina.
£75 - £90

R19-0103
Stylus (Bronze)
58mm
Good detail. Tip broken off.
£60 - £80

R19-0201
Stylus (Bronze)
155mm
Two heads set at each end.
Scarce in bronze. Large.
£70 - £80

R19-0202
Stylus (Iron)
114mm
Good condition. Iron stable.
£50 - £60

R19-0203
Stylus (Iron With Bronze
Inlay)
118mm
Inlaid bronze decoration. Iron
is substantially corrosion free.
£65 - £80

R19-0204
Stylus (Silver)
101mm
Decorated all along its length.
Rare in silver.
£200 - £250

R20-0101
Whistle (Two Heads)
40mm
Two outward facing heads.
Undoubtedly a whistle.
Very rare.
£200 - £250

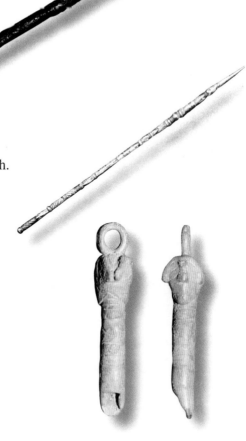

R20-0101(a)
Bell (Bronze) Solid
54mm
Typical Roman shape.
Remains of the iron clapper.
Even colour.
£40 - £50

R20-0102
Bell (Bronze) Solid
52mm
Remains of the iron clapper.
Patina a little ragged.
£35 - £40

R20-0103
Bell (Solid)
54mm
Remains of the iron clapper.
Patina a little patchy.
£35 - £40

R20-0104
Bell (Bronze) Solid
60mm
Good even patina. Remains of
the iron clapper.
£50 - £60

R20-0201
Bell (Openwork)
50mm
Bronze openwork bell.
Triangular cut-out shapes.
£30 - £40

R21-0101
Bronze Spoon
200mm
"Rat's tail" handle flat
spatula-like bowl.
Even patina.
£70 - £90

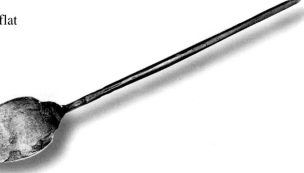

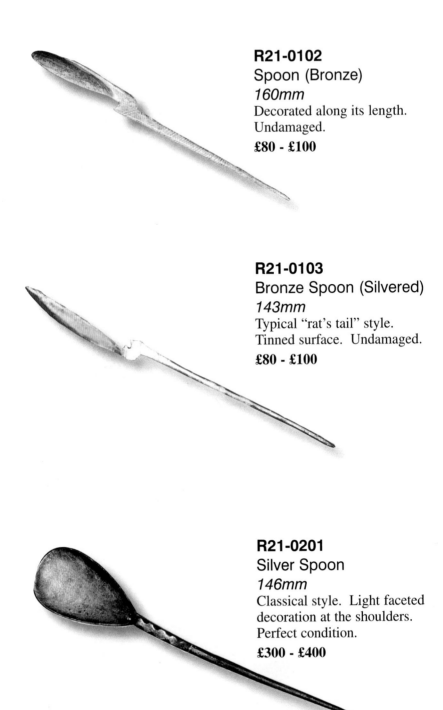

R21-0102
Spoon (Bronze)
160mm
Decorated along its length.
Undamaged.
£80 - £100

R21-0103
Bronze Spoon (Silvered)
143mm
Typical "rat's tail" style.
Tinned surface. Undamaged.
£80 - £100

R21-0201
Silver Spoon
146mm
Classical style. Light faceted
decoration at the shoulders.
Perfect condition.
£300 - £400

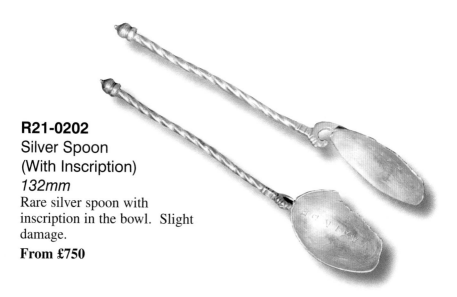

R21-0202
Silver Spoon
(With Inscription)
132mm
Rare silver spoon with
inscription in the bowl. Slight
damage.
From £750

R21-0301
Skillet (Bronze)
214mm
Complete and undamaged.
£600 - £700

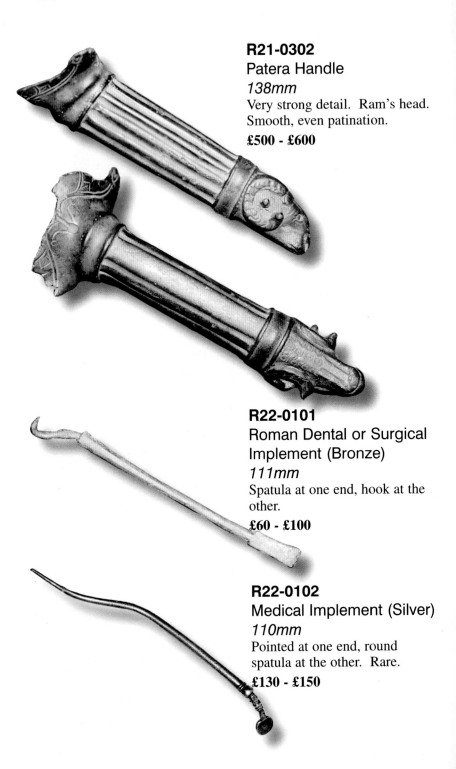

R21-0302
Patera Handle
138mm
Very strong detail. Ram's head.
Smooth, even patination.
£500 - £600

R22-0101
Roman Dental or Surgical
Implement (Bronze)
111mm
Spatula at one end, hook at the
other.
£60 - £100

R22-0102
Medical Implement (Silver)
110mm
Pointed at one end, round
spatula at the other. Rare.
£130 - £150

R22-0103
Medical Implement
(Silver)
55mm
Unusual style. Small size.
£80 - £125

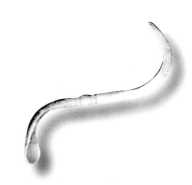

R22-0104
Medical Implement
(Bronze)
126mm
Surface a little rough. Slight
damage.
£50 - £60

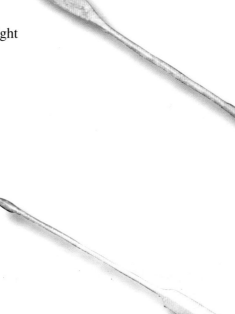

R22-0105
Medical Implement
(Bronze)
159mm
Smooth, even surface.
Undamaged.
£100 - £150

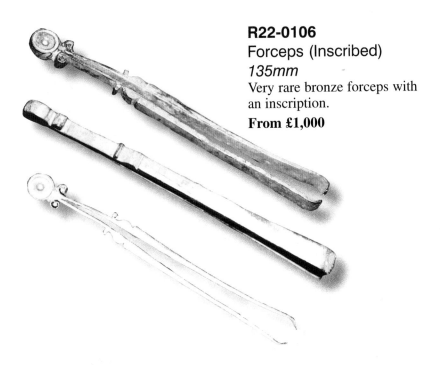

R22-0106
Forceps (Inscribed)
135mm
Very rare bronze forceps with an inscription.
From £1,000

R99-0101
Votive Axe
30mm
Bronze axe. Light decoration on the shaft. Even patina.
£30 - £40

R99-0102
Votive Axe
31mm
Bronze axe. Decoration on the blade. Good patina.
£35 - £45

R99-0103
Votive Axe
27mm
Socketed style. Patina a little
patchy.
£25 - £30

R99-0104
Votive Dagger
32mm
Even patina. Rare.
£40 - £50

R99-0105
Votive Axe
43mm
Typical style. A little nibbled
on the blade.
£30 - £40

R99-0106
Votive Axe
20mm
Looped and socketed type.
£35 - £45

R99-0107
Votive Axe
35mm
Decorated. Even patination.
£30 - £40

R99-0108
Votive Axe
37mm
Surface a little rough. Large size.
£35 - £45

R99-0109
Votive Axe
33mm
Decorated. Simple style.
£30 - £40

R99-0110
Votive Axe
23mm
Looped and socketed type. Surface a little ragged.
£20 - £30

R99-0111
Votive Axe
20mm
Looped and socketed type.
Flared blade.
£40 - £50

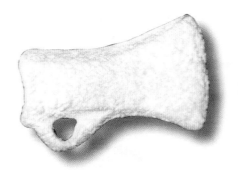

R99-0112
Votive Cauldron
27mm
Complete and undamaged.
£40 - £50

R99-0113
Votive Cauldron
25mm
One leg missing.
£30 - £40

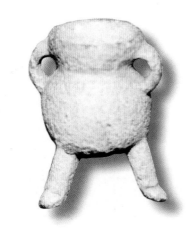

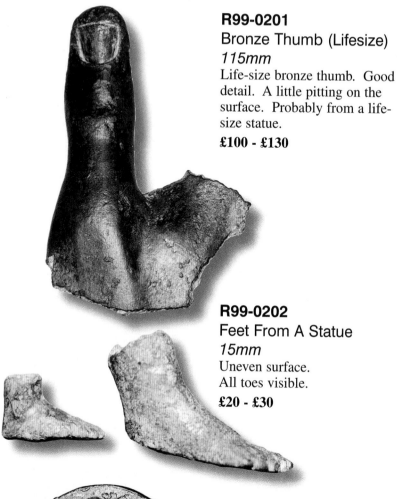

R99-0201
Bronze Thumb (Lifesize)
115mm
Life-size bronze thumb. Good detail. A little pitting on the surface. Probably from a life-size statue.

£100 - £130

R99-0202
Feet From A Statue
15mm
Uneven surface.
All toes visible.

£20 - £30

R99-0301
Mirror Back (Pan)
60mm dia
Silver mirror depicting Pan embracing a wood nymph. Good detail.

£400 - £500

R99-0401
Casket Leg (Lion's Head
& Paw)
72mm
Good detail. Dark even patina.
£130 - £180

R99-0402
Casket Leg
(Eagle's Claw)
55mm
Good detail. Winged eagle's
claw.
£80 - £100

R99-0501
Fragment
(With Inscription)
70mm
Piece of bronze bar with
inscription.
£25 - £30

R99-0601
Lead Plaque
(Sol & Other)
40mm
Some damage. Figure on
the right is
"Sol Invictus".
£80 - £100

THE ANGLO SAXONS

The year AD 407 saw the last Roman legions leaving Britain for active service elsewhere in Europe for the Empire, in disintegration, was fighting on all fronts. During this fifth century, an assortment of Germanic peoples took full advantage of Britain's now demilitarised state. By AD 600 Romano-Celtic Britain was a civilisation of the past and, in its place, the 'English' speaking invaders, namely the Saxons, Angles and Jutes, had re-drawn the political map. The Saxons ruled Essex, Wessex and Sussex, in other words the southern counties from west to east with the small exception of Kent which had been settled by the Jutes. The Angles controlled East Anglia, Mercia and Northumbria, in other words the midlands and north of England. Literacy became generally a skill of the past so archaeology and artefacts now become crucial in throwing light on these so-called 'Dark Ages'.

Thus, in understanding this period of our history, Anglo-Saxon sites, be they cemetery, settlement, palace or town, are of utmost importance. The last half of this twentieth century has seen many aspects of the history of this era being literally re-written thanks to diversified forms of new technology such as computers, radio carbon dating, DNA analysis, resistivity survey, magnetic survey and sonar radar. And then there is the metal detector which can, has and no doubt will locate sites where there had previously been no suspicion that a site existed. Metal detected coin finds have made us re-assess our views on the monetary system of the Dark Ages. Equally as important as the find of a rare coin is the find of a not so rare coin but in a location where there has so far been no evidence of Anglo Saxon settlement. This is because the Anglo Saxons did not travel far if they did not have to. Most communities produced for their own requirements with rare outings to trade with others or they would welcome the occasional itinerant merchant. Roads were unsafe places where bandits were forever on the look-out for easy pickings. Thus the odds would be against a found coin having been lost in transit but odds on there having been trading activity or coin storage nearby. It is the accurate reporting of such finds that continually adds to the sum of our Anglo Saxon knowledge.

Another metallic artefact found by detectorists which often is the bearer of useful information is jewellery. Most Anglo Saxons wore some form of metal adornment, varying in degree of finery according to wealth or lack of it, so the finding and recording of such accoutrements can convey much information. Strap ends, buckles, brooches, clasps were all worn in life, and death, by the various Teutonic tribes which settled here. But styles differed between them so comparisons between British and northern European finds assist in establishing settlement patterns of the various tribes. As with coins, a jewellery find in a location not known for any Anglo Saxon connection could prompt further investigation into the Dark Age history of that area.

But Anglo Saxon artefacts are not only harbingers of much needed information, they are items of beauty and highly collectable. The Anglo Saxon penchant for almost garish colour and decoration breathes life into every class of artefact. The Anglo Saxon sword for example with its iron blade and tang very often bore a hilt and pommel of bronze ornamented with precious metals. The many and varied classes of Anglo Saxon brooch, from the gilded and jewel encrusted circular brooches to silver plated cruciform brooches, attest to the skills of the Anglo Saxon craftsmen.

Anglo Saxon hairpins have elaborately decorated heads sometimes garnished with slices of garnet. Buckles become works of art and even combs are the subject of intricately carved decoration.

Anglo Saxon artefacts have always been popular amongst collectors, particularly if they are gilded or chip-carved. There is a distinct difference in style between the earlier Saxon objects (many of which have clearly Roman characteristics) and the later ones of the post-Viking period. It is this later period that produces many rare one-off artefacts that are difficult to find and even more difficult to value.

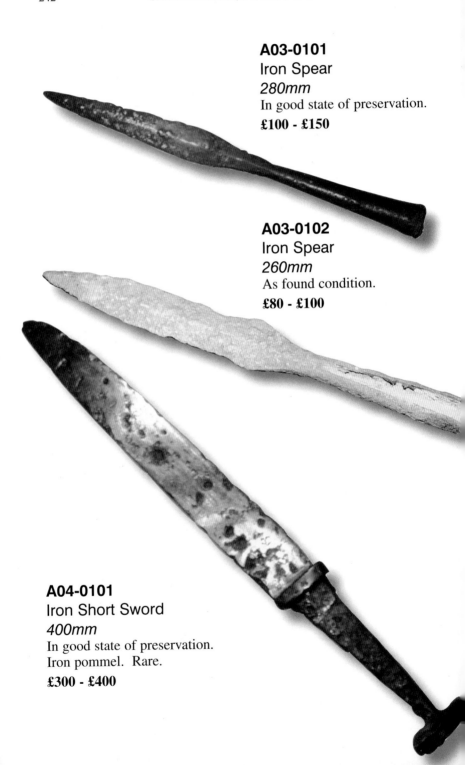

A03-0101
Iron Spear
280mm
In good state of preservation.
£100 - £150

A03-0102
Iron Spear
260mm
As found condition.
£80 - £100

A04-0101
Iron Short Sword
400mm
In good state of preservation.
Iron pommel. Rare.
£300 - £400

A04-0102
Pommel Cap
45mm
Pommel cap from a sword handle. One fixing eye broken.
£50 - £60

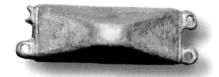

A04-0103
Sword (Iron)
835mm
In good state of preservation. Rare and complete.
From £800

A04-0201
Iron Knife
210mm
Quite pitted on the surface. Good shape.
£100 - £120

A04-0202
Pommel (Knife) Gilded
15mm
Gilding intact. Face in the centre.
£150 - £200

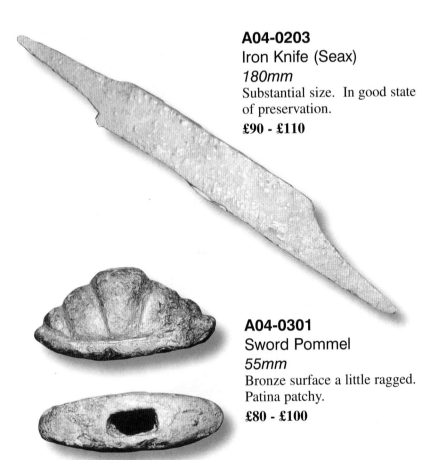

A04-0203
Iron Knife (Seax)
180mm
Substantial size. In good state
of preservation.

£90 - £110

A04-0301
Sword Pommel
55mm
Bronze surface a little ragged.
Patina patchy.

£80 - £100

A04-0302
Sword Pommel
60mm
Bronze even patina. Smooth
surface.

£100 - £130

A04-0303
Bronze Pommel
(Silver Inlay)
100mm
Very large and heavy.
Intricate silver inlay with
niello. Very rare.
From £7,000

A05-0101
Iron Shield Boss
120mm dia
Three rivets remaining. Slight
break on one edge. Good state
of preservation.
£150 - £200

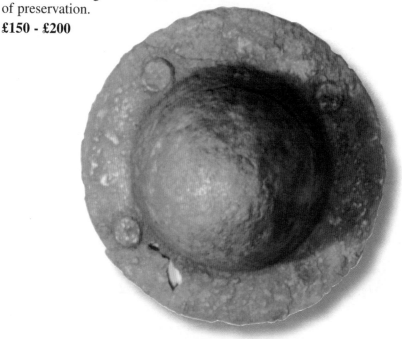

A05-0102
Iron Shield Boss
150mm dia
Complete apart from a
small nick on the edge.
£140 - £180

A05-0103
Iron Shield Boss
170mm dia
Four rivet holes. One
rivet remaining.
Unusual spike in the
centre. Good state of
preservation.
£250 - £300

A05-0104
Iron Shield Boss
145mm dia
Three silver discs around the
rim and one in the centre.
Slight damage.
£150 - £180

A06-0101
Silver Pin (Gilded)
58mm
Some of the gilding remaining.
Undamaged.
£75 - £100

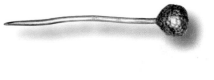

A06-0102
Pin Head (Silver Gilt) With Stones
16mm dia
Filigree decoration. Most of
the gilding remaining. Some
of the stones missing. Rare.
£100 - £150

A06-0103
Pin Head (Bronze Gilt)
22mm
A little ragged. Stones set in
the protruding stems.
£80 - £100

A06-0104
Pin Head (Gilded) Silver
18mm
Three birds' heads holding a
ball. Most gilding remaining.
£200 - £250

A06-0201
Bronze Pin
(Faceted Head)
60mm
Ring and dot decoration on the
hexagonal head. Even patina.
£20 - £30

A06-0301
Bone Pin
79mm
Complete and undamaged.
£25 - £30

A06-0302
Bone Pin Beater
140mm
Unusual and scarce
£40 - £50

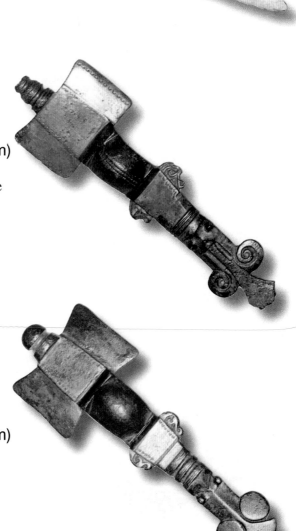

A07-0101
Brooch (Cruciform)
138mm
Long brooch. Square
head plate with
decoration along the
edges. Even patina.
£350 - £450

A07-0102
Brooch (Cruciform)
125mm
Long brooch.
Complete and
undamaged.
Even patina.
£400 - £500

A07-0103
Brooch (Cruciform)
112mm
Long brooch. Surface a little pitted. Even patina.
£300 - £375

A07-0104
Brooch (Small Long Type)
60mm
Cruciform style. Good, even patina.
£75 - £85

A07-0105
Brooch (Small Long Type)
75mm
Complete and undamaged. Even patina.
£100 - £150

A07-0106
Brooch (Cruciform) Broken
120mm
50% gilding remaining. Broken in places.
£200 - £300

A07-0107
Brooch (Part of)
Cruciform
35mm
Part of a cruciform brooch
showing a face. 50% gilding
remaining. Slight damage.
£50 - £75

A07-0108
Chip Carved Piece (From
a Cruciform)
30mm
Face in the centre. 50% of the
gilding remaining.
£70 - £80

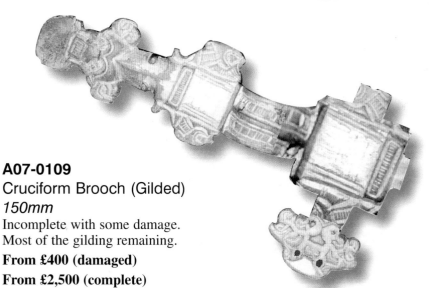

A07-0109
Cruciform Brooch (Gilded)
150mm
Incomplete with some damage.
Most of the gilding remaining.
From £400 (damaged)
From £2,500 (complete)

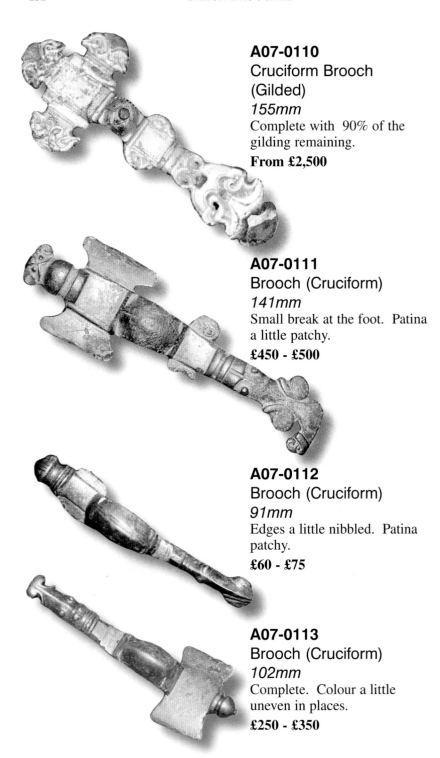

A07-0110
Cruciform Brooch
(Gilded)
155mm
Complete with 90% of the gilding remaining.
From £2,500

A07-0111
Brooch (Cruciform)
141mm
Small break at the foot. Patina a little patchy.
£450 - £500

A07-0112
Brooch (Cruciform)
91mm
Edges a little nibbled. Patina patchy.
£60 - £75

A07-0113
Brooch (Cruciform)
102mm
Complete. Colour a little uneven in places.
£250 - £350

A07-0114
Brooch (Cruciform)
121mm
Complete. Traces of iron on
the surface.
£450 - £550

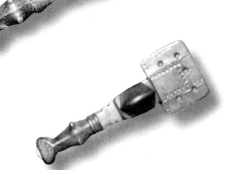

A07-0115
Small Long Brooch
81mm
Smooth, even surface with rich
green patina. Unusual style.
£350 - £400

A07-0116
Small Long Brooch
78mm
Surface a little rough. Signs of
pitting.
£70 - £80

A07-0117
Brooch (Small Long
Type) Pair
75mm
Matching pair with even,
smooth surface.
£300 - £350

A07-0118
Brooch (Small Long
Type) Pair
74mm
Matching pair. Surface a little
uneven.
£250 - £300

A07-0119
Brooch (Small Long
Type)
75mm
Complete. Slight bend near
the base of the foot.
£90 - £110

A07-0120
Brooch (Small Long
Type)
68mm
Patina patchy in places.
£60 - £75

A07-0121
Brooch (Small Long
Type)
69mm
Decorated over most of the
surfaces.
£100 - £120

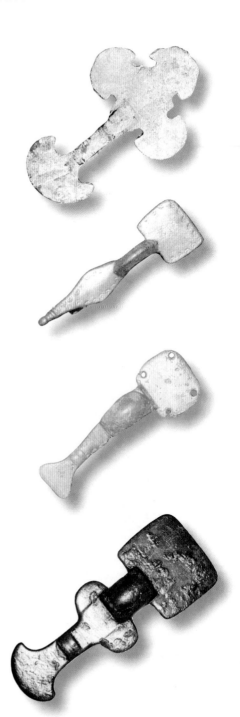

A07-0122
Brooch (Cruciform)
82mm
Surface very ragged. Unusual, large flared foot.

£120 - £150

A07-0123
Small Square Headed Brooch
66mm
Smooth, even surface. Good patina.

£60 - £70

A07-0124
Brooch (Small Long Type)
70mm
Four pierced holes around the head plate. Slight bend in the main body.

£60 - £70

A07-0201
Brooch (Square Headed)
82mm
Small long brooch with a square top plate. Some corrosion on the surface.

£100 - £130

A07-0202
Brooch (Part of) Silver Gilt
51mm
Broken piece from a silver square headed brooch.
£70 - £90

A07-0203
Square Headed Brooch
145mm
Complete and undamaged. Gilding missing. Even patina.
P.O.A.

A07-0204
Square Headed Brooch
120mm
Over 75% of gilding
remaining. Well detailed.
Surface a little rough in places.
From £3,000

A07-0205
Square Headed Brooch
115mm
Bottom part broken away.
Other damage present.
Museum documented.
£300 - £400

A07-0206
Brooch (Radiate Head)
Bronze Gilded
60mm
Small break at the foot.
Heavily gilded. Museum
documented.
£350 - £400

A07-0207
Brooch (Square Headed)
42mm
Small size. Most of the
gilding remaining.
£60 - £70

A07-0208
Brooch (Radiate Head)
58mm
Smooth surface. Even patina.
Highly decorated. Museum
documented.
£300 - £350

A07-0301
Brooch (Equal-Arm)
Broken
75mm
One half of an equal arm
brooch. Much gilding
remaining. Broken at one end.
Large size.
£125 - £175

A07-0302
Brooch
(Equal-Armed)
45mm
Ring and dot decoration.
Even patina.
£40 - £60

A07-0303
Equal Ended Brooch
50mm
Patina a little ragged.
£20 - £30

A07-0304
Brooch
(Equal Armed)
60mm
Complete with its pin
still in situ.
£80 - £100

A07-0305
Brooch
(With Garnets)
27mm
Bronze double headed
with garnets set in the
eyes. Rare.
£350 - £400

A07-0306
Caterpillar Brooch
35mm
Typical style. Fairly basic.
£30 - £40

A07-0307
Brooch (Equal Armed)
44mm
£25 - £30

A07-0401
Brooch (Disc & Pins
Type)
31mm
Part of a disc-and-pins
type brooch.
£80 - £90

A07-0402
Brooch (Interlace Design)
Disc Type
28mm dia
Patina a little patchy. Pin
missing.
£60 - £80

A07-0403
Brooch (Disc Type)
Chip-carved
34mm dia
Stones missing from recesses.
At least 50% gilding remains.
£150 - £200

A07-0404
Brooch (Disc Type)
22mm
Cross design in centre.
Lacking patination.
£25 - £30

A07-0405
Brooch (Disc Type)
32mm dia
Beast looking back. Patina
fairly even.
£60 - £80

A07-0406
Brooch (Disc Type)
28mm
Beast looking back. Ring and dot decoration.
£80 - £100

A07-0407
Brooch (Disc Type)
28mm
Beast looking back. Patina patchy.
£80 - £100

A07-0408
Brooch (Disc Type)
30mm dia
Beast looking back. Sharp
detail. Even patina.

£100 - £130

A07-0409
Brooch (Interlace Design)
29mm
Even patina. Sharp detail.
interlace design.

£90 - £120

A07-0410
Brooch (Interlace Design)
29mm
Patina a little patchy. Weak
detail.
£70 - £80

A07-0411
Brooch (Disc Type)
28mm
Smooth, even patina. unusual
type.
£90 - £110

A07-0412
Brooch (Cross)
28mm
Expanding cross design. Even
patina.
£70 - £90

A07-0413
Brooch (Disc Type)
50mm dia
Open-work design of a cross.
Surface a little uneven.
£100 - £125

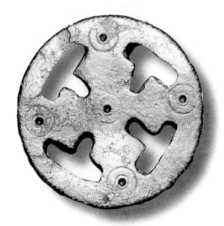

A07-0414
Brooch (Disc Type)
31mm dia
Fully gilded. Silvered around
the perimeter and in the centre.
Complete and undamaged.
£400 - £450

A07-0415
Brooch (Silver) Disc Type
34mm dia
Silver. Chip carved entwined
beast design. Gold gilded.
£500 - £600

A07-0416
Brooch (Silver & Gold)
32mm dia
Gold and silver with garnets.
Inlaid intricate design. Very
rare.
From £8,000

A07-0501
Brooch (Button Type)
Saucer
21mm dia
Face in the centre is of typical
style. Much of the gilding
remains.
£150 - £195

A07-0502
Brooch (Button Type)
Saucer
18mm dia
Face in the centre is of typical style. Nearly all of the gilding remains.
£150 - £195

A07-0503
Brooch (Saucer Type)
38mm
Gilt bronze with most of the gilding remaining. A little "nibbled" around the edge.
£190 - £250

A07-0504
Brooch (Saucer Type)
36mm dia
Gilt bronze with scroll decoration. A little "nibbled" around the edge.
One of a pair (see A07-0506).
£250 - £350

A07-0505
Brooch (Saucer Type)
27mm dia
Gilding virtually intact.
Remains of iron pin on reverse.
Decorated with
geometric patterns.
£500 - £600

A07-0506
Brooch (Saucer Type)
35mm dia
One of a pair (see A07-0504).
Edge a little ragged.
£200 - £300

A07-0507
Brooch (Saucer Type)
35mm dia
Central boss with a stylised
zoomorphic motif around.
Much of the gilding remaining.
Hole pierced at the top.
Perhaps worn as a pendant.
£250 - £325

A07-0508
Brooch (Saucer Type)
25mm
Sun-like face in the centre.
Most gilding remaining.
£400 - £500

A07-0509
Button Brooch (Gilded)
15mm
Face in the centre. Virtually
all gilding remaining.
£150 - £200

A07-0601
Annular Brooch (Bronze)
45mm dia
Edges a little ragged. Ring
and dot decoration. Large size.
£35 - £45

A07-0801
Coin Brooch (Lead-Alloy)
24mm dia
Plate brooch imitating a coin obverse. Rare.
£400 - £500

A07-0802
Brooch (Human Face)
30mm
Face in the centre. Four protruding lugs (one missing). Traces of enamel.
£50 - £75

A07-0803
Brooch (Gilded) Axe Shaped
38mm
Unusual brooch, possibly an adaptation of a larger item. Border of interlace design. Bronze fixing pin intact.
£300 - £400

A07-0804
Brooch (Head) Pewter
38mm dia
Aethelred II style portrait. A
little damage. Rare.
£300 - £400

A07-0805
Penannular Brooch
30mm
Smooth, even patina. Pin
intact. scarce.
£60 - £80

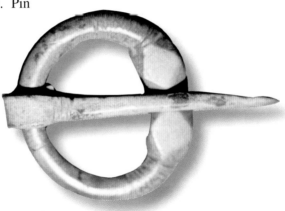

A07-0806
Brooch (Bird)
30mm
Smooth surface and even
patina. Scarce type.
£120 - £150

A08-0101
Bronze Pendant (Gilded)
34mm
Swastika design in the centre.
Suspension loop broken. Most
of the gilding remains. Rare.
£150 - £225

A08-0102
Bronze Pendant
(Enamelled)
40mm
Face with red enamel set in the
cheeks. Bulbous eyes and
curly moustache. Rare.
£600 - £700

A08-0103
Pendant Bronze (Gilded)
16mm dia
Suspension loop broken. Most
gilding remaining.
£100 - £120

A08-0201
Silver Pendant (Gilded)
22mm
Fully gilded with the letters
LA/AG. Large suspension
loop. Cross design.
£100 - £150

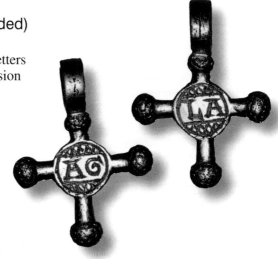

A08-0301
Bronze Pendant Hanger
(Gilded)
53mm
Four birds' heads with a
central chip-carved design.
Virtually all of the gilding
intact. Rare.
£400 - £500

A08-0302
Pendant Hanger
34mm
In the form of a crouching
animal. Gilded.
£120 - £150

A08-0401
Gold Pendant (With Garnets)
30mm dia
Central garnet surrounded by three triangular shaped garnets (one missing). Filigree ornament. A little damage.

From £3,000

A08-0402
Gold Pendant (Garnet and Shell)
28mm dia
Central garnet in a gold mount set on a white shell boss. Scroll filigree ornament. Damaged at lower edge.

From £2,500

A08-0403
Gold Pendant (With Garnet)
24mm dia
Central garnet. Filigree ornament. Repair carried out on suspension loop.

From £1,800

A08-0404
Gold Pendant
(With Garnet)
20mm dia
Dark garnet set in a gold
mount. Complete and
undamaged.
From £1,200

A08-0405
Gold Pendant
(With Garnet)
22mm
Pear shaped pendant. Light
damage on one edge.
From £900

A08-0406
Gold Pendant
(With Garnet)
26mm
Set with a flat topped,
large deep red garnet.
From £1,000

A08-0407
Gold Pendant
(With Garnet)
21mm
Set with a deep red, flat topped
garnet. Pendant complete and
undamaged.
From £1,300

A08-0408
Gold Pendant (Garnets)
23mm
White enamel with flat inlaid
garnets all around. Rare type.
£2,000 - £2,500

A08-0409
Gold Pendant (Coin)
17mm
Gold coin formed into a
pendant.
£1,000 - £1,300

A08-0410
Gold Pendant
(With Garnet)
21mm dia
Garnet set in the centre.
Simple design.
£1,500 - £2,000

A08-0411
Pendant Spacer (Gold)
20mm
Spacer from a necklace.
Slightly mis-shapen.
£150 - £200

A09-0101
Mount (With Garnet)
Gilded Bronze
23mm dia
Decorative bronze mount with
most of the gilding remaining.
Garnet in the centre.
£250 - £350

A09-0102
Bronze Mount
(Gilded & Tinned)
36mm
Face design. Gilded and
tinned.
£50 - £75

A09-0103
Bronze Mount (Gilded)
57mm
Hatched box design in the
centre with faces at each end.
30% gilding remaining.
£80 - £100

A09-0104
Bronze Mount (Gilded)
31mm
Decorative mount. 50%
gilding remaining.
£50 - £75

A09-0105
Bronze Mount (Gilded)
26mm
Ferret-like face design. Most
of the gilding remaining.
£60 - £80

A09-0106
Mount (Bird's Head)
Gilded
28mm
Most of the gilding remaining.
Complete and undamaged.
£400 - £450

A09-0107
Mount (Rectangular)
31mm
Zoomorphic moulded panels
and remains of enamel inlays.
No gilding remaining.
£150 - £225

A09-0108
Mount (Scabbard)
Bronze
50mm
Gilded and silvered mount.
Probably from a scabbard.
£100 - £125

A09-0109
Mount (Gilded)
Bronze
60mm
Most of the gilding
remains. Depicts two
entwined birds or
serpents. Complete and
undamaged.
£400 - £500

A09-0110
Mount (Bowl)
26mm dia
Tribrach pattern.
Silvery surfaces with traces of
red enamel.
£75 - £100

A09-0111
Mount (Two Birds)
30mm dia
Bronze mount with engraved
detail of two birds feeding on
branches, all within a border.
£150 - £190

A09-0112
Mount (Gilded) Face
17mm dia
Most of the gilding remaining.
Chip-carved face in the centre.
£150 - £195

A09-0113
Pyramid Mount (Bronze)
15mm
Garnet set into the top. Even
patina.
£90 - £125

A09-0114
Bronze Mount (Gilded)
29mm dia
Stone missing from the centre.
Most of the gilding remaining.
A little pitting on the surface.
£250 - £350

A09-0115
Mount (Chip-Carved)
Gilded
35mm
Fragment from a larger piece.
Edges a little ragged.
£50 - £60

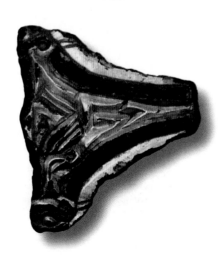

A09-0116
Mount (Gilded) Bronze
25mm
Fantastic animal in the centre.
Fully gilded.
£120 - £150

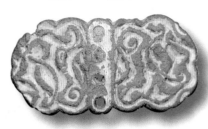

A09-0117
Mount (Gilded)
40mm
Surface a little rough.
Gilding in the recesses.
£100 - £130

A09-0118
Bronze Mount (Gilded)
52mm
Chip-carved with garnet set in
the centre. Slight damage at
each end.
£300 - £350

A09-0119
Mount
35mm
Red enamel and gold gilding
remain. Broken fragment.
£120 - £150

A09-0120
Mount (Gilded) Bronze
35mm
Fully gilded bird with curled
beak.
£350 - £400

A09-0121
Mount (Face) Gilded
Bronze
24mm
Fragment depicting a human
face.
£120 - £150

A09-0122
Mount (Square)
17mm
Small mount. Surface a little
pitted.
£90 - £110

A09-0123
Mount (Face)
17mm
Small mount. Face in the
centre.
£90 - £120

A09-0124
Mount (Gilded)
39mm dia
Heavily gilded round mount.
Cross separating four panels
with foliate design.
£350 - £400

A09-0125
Mount (Helmet)
47mm
Heavy bronze bell-shaped
mount. Most of the gold gilding remaining.
£600 - £700

A09-0126
Mount (Chip Carved)
Gilded
31mm
Fragment fully gilded.
£70 - £80

A09-0127
Mount
34mm
Unusual mount with protruding arms forming a cross. Chip-carved, gold-gilded centre.
£250 - £300

A09-0128
Mount (Gilded) Bronze
35mm
Two birds' heads with interlace design between. Surface a little rough.
£200 - £250

A09-0129
Mount (Bronze Gilded)
18mm
Small sized mount. Silvered surface. Simple design.
£100 - £130

A09-0130
Bronze Mount (Gilded)
35mm
Slight damage. Cross design in the centre.
£100 - £130

A09-0131
Scabbard Mount
30mm
Iron with silver inlay and niello. Rare.
£200 - £250

A09-0132
Mount
44mm dia
Large chip-carved mount. Slight damage on one edge.
£300 - £450

A09-0133
Two Mounts
20mm
One better than the other in this matching pair.

£60 - £70 the pair

A09-0134
Mount (Wolf)
30mm
Possibly the top of a pin. Unusual.

£80 - £90

A09-0135
Mount (Harness) Enamelled
53mm
Harness mount. Enamelled with traces of gilding.

£80 - £100

A09-0136
Mount (See Sutton Hoo Mound 17)
34mm
Smooth, even green patina. Good detail.

£240 - £275

A09-0137
Mount (Rock Crystal)
22mm
Rock crystal set into a mount.
Traces of gold gilt.
£50 - £60

A09-0138
Hanging Bowl Mount
(Enamelled)
61mm
Rare mount. Fully enamelled
in the form of a bird.
£600 - £700

A09-0201
Pyramid Mount (Silver)
15mm
Garnet missing from the top of
pyramid. Triangular recesses
are gilded. Undamaged. Rare.
£300 - £400

A09-0202
Pyramid Mount (Silver)
10mm
Small size with niello inlay.
£150 - £200

A09-0203
Mount (Silver Inlay)
60mm
Large mount with a beast's head at each of the four corners and with four inlaid panels.
£600 - £750

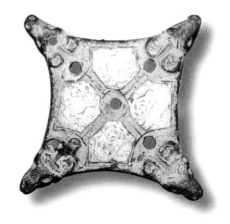

A09-0204
Silver Mount (Bird)
22mm
Undamaged with niello inlay. Rare.
£250 - £350

A10-0101
Silver Finger Ring
18mm dia
Typical form of twisted wire.
Undamaged.
£150 - £195

A10-0102
Silver Ring (Inscription)
19mm dia
Inscribed on the outside with
the letters L.A.A.G.
£150 - £200

A10-0103
Gold Finger Ring
14mm
Small size. Very unusual style.
£170 - £200

A12-0101
Strap-End (3 Rivets)
35mm
Bronze interlaced design.
Even patina.
£30 - £40

A12-0102
Strap-End (Silver Inlay)
68mm
Large bronze strap-end. Panels
of silver inlay. Dark, smooth
patina.
£175 - £250

A12-0103
Strap-End
29mm
Bronze, decorative design.
£30 - £40

A12-0104
Strap-End (Silver Rivets)
41mm
Wheel like motif in the centre.
Silver rivets. Even patina.
£60 - £80

A12-0105
Strap-End (Silver Rivets)
38mm
Glass beads in the eyes (one missing). Unusual fixing lug on the underside. Even patina. Silver rivets.

£250 - £300

A12-0106
Strap-End (Silver Inlay)
45mm
Banded silver inlay. Even patina.

£125 - £150

A12-0107
Strap-End (Silver Inlay)
34mm
Bronze with an inlaid panel of niello decoration.

£75 - £95

A12-0108
Strap-End (Silver Inlay)
40mm
Bronze with inlaid panels of silver. Dark patina.

£175 - £225

A12-0109
Strap-End (Silver Inlay)
40mm
Bronze with silver inlay. One rivet hole broken.
£125 - £150

A12-0110
Strap-End (Silver Inlay)
38mm
Bronze with inlaid linear detail. Good patina.
£75 - £95

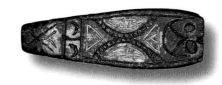

A12-0111
Strap-End (Silver Inlay)
47mm
Bronze with silver inlay.
£50 - £60

A12-0112
Strap-End (Silver Inlay)
56mm
Bronze with traces of silver inlay. Exaggerated ears. Even, dark patina.
£125 - £150

A12-0113
Strap-End (Silver Inlay)
Equal Ended
53mm
Bronze with silver panel in the centre and silver inlay on each head. Even patina. Rare.
£400 - £500

A12-0114
Strap-End (Enamel Inlay)
39mm
Bronze with two enamel inserts. Dark, even patina.
£40 - £50

A12-0115
Strap-End (Zig Zag Pattern)
51mm
Bronze with zig-zag decoration. Good patina.
£40 - £50

A12-0116
Strap-End (Enamel Inlay)
34mm
Bronze with beast design and enamel inlay.
£75 - £95

A12-0117
Strap-End (Silver Inlay)
51mm
Bronze with silver inlay showing a crude face. Even patina.
£70 - £90

A12-0118
Strap-End (Silver Inlay)
32mm
Bronze with inlaid silver scroll patterns.
£70 - £90

A12-0119
Strap-End (Three Animal Heads)
58mm
Bronze with three moulded animal masks. Even patina.
£100 - £125

A12-0120
Strap-End (Lug Underneath)
40mm
Bronze with protruding lug on the underside. Even patina.
£50 - £60

A12-0121
Strap-End (Gold Inlay)
42mm
Bronze with an inset panel of
gold. Even green patina.
£150 - £195

A12-0122
Strap-End (With Runes)
45mm
Glass stones in the eyes.
Runic inscription on the
underside. Slight pitting on
the surface. Very rare.
From £750

A12-0123
Various Strap-Ends
Largest 50mm
£20 - £40 each.

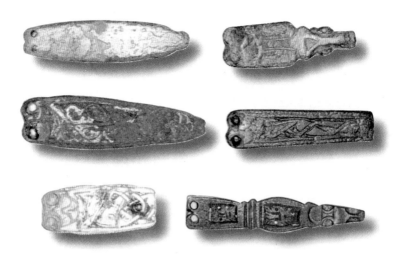

A12-0124
Strap-End (Bronze)
45mm
Surface a little uneven.
Simple design.

£30 - £40

A12-0125
Strap-End (Bronze)
47mm
Unusual type with long ears
which curl at the end.

£70 - £80

A12-0126
Strap-End (Silver Inlay)
41mm
Beads inlaid in the eyes.
Good style.

£80 - £90

A12-0127
Strap-End (Enamel Inlay)
38mm
Single rivet. Smooth, even
patina.

£40 - £50

A12-0128
Strap-End (Silver Inlay)
51mm
Large size. Two silver panels with scrollwork design.
£80 - £90

A12-0129
Strap-End (Silver Inlay)
44mm
Good, smooth patina. Some of the silver inlay damaged.
£125 - £150

A12-0201
Strap-End (Silver) Silver Inlay
45mm
Silver with niello inlay. Slight fracture across the centre. Rare.
£700 - £800

A12-0202
Silver Strap-End (Trewhiddle)
43mm
Silver trewhiddle style beasts and interlace design. Undamaged. Rare.
From £900

A12-0203
Strap-End (Silver) Broken
30mm
Silver. Broken. Good detail.
£75 - £100

A12-0204
Silver Strap-End
46mm
Silver with glass bead eyes.
Good detail. Undamaged.
From £1,000

A12-0205
Strap-End (Silver)
32mm
Small size with niello inlay.
Complete.
£600 - £700

A12-0206
Strap-End (Silver)
40mm
Average size and complete.
£650 - £750

A12-0207
Strap-End (Silver)
40mm
With full gold gilding and
undamaged.
£350 - £450

A12-0301
Buckle (Centre Silvered)
70mm
Openwork belt-plate decorated
with a silvered centre motif.
Complete and undamaged.
£125 - £150

A12-0302
Buckle (Glass Inlay)
Merovingian
65mm
Incised decoration on the plate with glass inlay in one of the recesses. Good, even patina.
£100 - £140

A12-0303
Buckle (Scorpion)
44mm
In the form of a scorpion. Complete and undamaged. Ring and dot decoration. Good, even patina. Rare.
£150 - £200

A12-0304
Buckle (With Pin)
26mm
Ring and dot decoration. Basic design.
£20 - £30

A12-0305
Buckle (With Garnets)
25mm
Damaged. Surface a little rough. Three flat garnets remaining.

£125 - £150

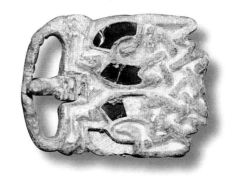

A12-0306
Buckle (Silver)
40mm
Typical style. Undamaged.

£100 - £120

A12-0307
Buckle (Bronze)
40mm
Good, even patination. Rivets still in place.

£75 - £85

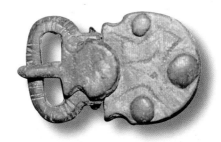

A12-0308
Buckle (With Plate)
75mm
Large size. Two fantastic animals in the centre panel. Complete.

£400 - £450

A12-0309
Buckle
48mm
Smooth surface. Even patina.
£70 - £90

A12-0310
Buckle
42mm
Traces of gilding. Surface a
little rough.
£100 - £120

A12-0311
Buckle
92mm
Very large buckle. Patina
patchy in places. Two studs
remaining.
£250 - £300

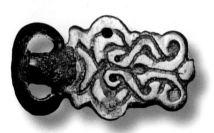

A12-0312
Buckle
50mm
Bronze buckle. Traces of iron
around the pin.
£100 - £120

A12-0313
Buckle (Silvered)
80mm
Large buckle with elaborate design. Surface a little rough.
£200 - £250

A12-0401
Buckle (With Garnet)
38mm
Bowed frame type. Garnet inset into the pin.
£70 - £90

A12-0402
Buckle (Silvered)
34mm
Bronze with a silvered surface.
£70 - £80

A12-0403
Silver Buckle
(With Rivets)
32mm
Silver buckle with
rivets from the
plate.
£80 - £100

A12-0501
Buckle Plate
(Trewhiddle)
32mm
Strap-end plate. Trewhiddle
style beast. Good, even patina.
£75 - £95

A12-0502
Buckle Plate
41mm
Bronze with a face in the centre. Rough surface.
£60 - £70

A13-0201
Clothes Fastener (Silver)
45mm
Three panels with a beast in each one. Intricate design.
£350 - £500

A14-0101
Bronze Tweezers (With Loop)
61mm
Patina flaking a little.
£30 - £40

A14-0102
Bronze Tweezers (With Loop)
80mm
Decorated. Good, even patina.
£50 - £60

A14-0103
Bronze Tweezers
70mm
Decorated. Good, even patina.
£50 - £60

A17-0101
Bronze Key
38mm
Large plain disc handle and
simple wards. Good, even
patina.
£60 - £70

A17-0102
Bronze Key
50mm
Suspension loop at top.
Even patina.
£80 - £100

A17-0103
Bronze Key
42mm
Typical form.
Good even
patina.
£70 - £80

A17-0104
Bronze Key (Lyre Key)
62mm
Tuning key for a lyre or
similar musical instrument.
Decorated on the face. Rare.
£125 - £150

A17-0105
Key (Zoomorphic)
70mm
Unusual zoomorphic key with openwork handle. Simple ward.
£200 - £250

A17-0106
Key
48mm
Fairly worn. Smooth, even surface. Simple design.
£60 - £70

A17-0107
Bronze Key
40mm
Open-work lozenge handle. Very long ward.
£50 - £60

A19-0101
Stylus (Bronze)
45mm
Bronze stylus adapted to form a brooch or pin. Rare.
£150 - £200

A20-0101
Bell (Bronze)
29mm
Cut-out triangles. Iron clapper still in place.
£40 - £50

A99-0101
Lead Spindle Whorl
30mm dia
Decorated on both sides.
£25 - £30

A99-0102
Spindle Whorl (Runic)
Lead
33mm dia
Domed shape, with runic inscription around the surface.
£200 - £300

A99-0201
Girdle Hangers
(Complete)
140mm
Pair of girdle hangers, one
slightly bent but otherwise
complete.
£200 - £250

A99-0202
Girdle Hanger
127mm
Decorated all along its surface.
£80 - £120

A99-0203
Belt Fitting
(Found With Coin)
30mm
Beast biting its tail. Smooth,
even patina.
£120 - £150

THE VIKINGS

As admitted by the eminent archaeologist and anthropologist Dr. Julian Richards, "the Vikings themselves can be elusive to the archaeologist." Equally, Viking artefacts are rarely found by detectorists which is reflected by the limited size of our Viking section compared with those of other periods in our history. This rarity is also reflected in the excellent prices which can be obtained especially where the artefact is a good example of Viking art of which there are various named "schools" and which vary from stylized, repeated animal motifs to patterns of flora, fauna, ribbons and tendrils. This art, applied to metal, wood, bone, pottery and glass, is vivacious and vibrant, intricate and interesting, fussy yet fine.

Viking stirrup mounts seem to turn up more frequently than any other individual Viking find and in a variety of styles. Brooches are far rarer and, like the stirrup mounts, reflect the wide variety of Viking art. Viking women wore the 'tortoise' shaped brooch to fasten over-shifts and from which would hang personal utensils or ornaments. Other shapes of brooch would be the circular disc or the popular trefoil, three lobed brooch, often worn at the neck. At variance to these solid, decorated types, the open ring-and-pin brooch was a typical male cloak-fastening and Viking open-work zoomorphic brooches are amongst the finest of this category of practical jewellery.

Purely ornamental jewellery was highly favoured by The Vikings as well. Such display was not only intended to enhance personal appearance, but was also worn to indicate personal wealth. Thus Viking credit-rating would be reflected in the amount and quality of brooches, necklaces, neck rings, pendants, bracelets, and armbands. Such personal adornment worn by a wealthy Viking would be in handcrafted gold and silver.

At the other end of the social scale, personal adornment would have been equally as decorative but Viking design would have been applied to mass produced items in bronze or even pewter. Nor were the Vikings above 'fake jewellery' for they were adept at plating base metals with silver or tin to give an impression of solid silver. Additionally, gilding has been found on silver and on bronze, perhaps to suggest more gold ownership than was actually true?

Beyond personal ornamentation, other surviving but extremely rare metal artefacts are the weapons which, as with all warrior races, their owners held dear; and these weapons could be decorated to the same degree as the metal which they wore. Smaller metal Viking finds bearing their unique designs include horse trappings, mounts, strap ends and buckles.

V07-0101
Disc Brooch (Gilded)
Bronze
30mm dia
50% of the gilding remaining.
Sharp detail.
£150 - £195

V07-0102
Disc Brooch (Cloisonné)
25mm dia
Cross design in the centre. All
seven lugs remain, five of
which still have their glass
insets. Pin and catchplate
intact. Traces of gilding.
£200 - £250

V07-0103
Disc Brooch (Cloisonné)
24mm dia
Cross design in the centre. No
protruding lugs. Traces of
gilding. Pin missing.
£175 - £225

V07-0104
Disc Brooch (Cloisonne)
24mm
Six lugs around, four of which still have their glass insets. Most gilding remains.
£230 - £275

V07-0105
Disc Brooch (Cloisonne)
25mm dia
Surface a little rough but glass inlay all remains.
£120 - £150

V07-0106
Disc Brooch (Cloisonne)
28mm dia
Praying figure in the centre. Scarce type.
£250 - £300

V07-0107
Disc Brooch (Gilded)
23mm dia
Surface a little rough. Most gilding remaining.
£150 - £175

V07-0108
Brooch (Disc Type)
25mm dia
Same design as V07-0107 but different type of brooch, without gilding.
£150 - £175

V07-0109
Disc Brooch (Enamelled)
28mm
Red enamelled face in the centre. Rare type.
£150 - £200

V07-0201
Trefoil Brooch (Bronze)
42mm
Incised decoration.
Even patina.
£200 - £250

V07-0202
Trefoil Brooch (Bronze)
48mm
Interlaced design.
Even patina.
£225 - £295

V07-0203
Trefoil Brooch (Silver)
50mm
Interlaced design is quite worn.
Probably three beasts. Traces
of iron on the reverse. Rare in
silver.
From £1,000

V07-0204
Trefoil Brooch (Bronze)
43mm
Interlaced design.
Even patina.
£300 - £400

V07-0301
Brooch (Eagle)
30mm
Light decoration. Pin missing.
Even green patina.
£100 - £125

V07-0302
Brooch (Silver) Gilded
38mm
Pin intact. Most of the gilding
remaining. Very rare.
From £2,000

V07-0303
Brooch (Bronze)
50mm
Very rare brooch. Rotate it to
see different beasts depicted.
Even patina.
£600 - £750

V07-0304
Brooch (Cockerel)
40mm
Surface a little rough. Rare type.
Museum documented.
£350 - £400

V08-0101
Pendant (Bronze)
38mm
In the form of a woman
(Valkyrie) holding a spear and
shield. Undamaged. Rare.
£400 - £500

V08-0102
Pendant (Raven)
44mm
Traces of gilding. Surface a
little rough.
£130 - £175

V09-0101
Mount (Stirrup)
46mm
Single central head of a bat-like creature. Even patina.
£70 - £80

V09-0102
Mount (Stirrup)
34mm
Three heads. Patina a little ragged.
£50 - £60

V09-0103
Mount (Stirrup)
35mm
Central single head. Even patina.
£60 - £70

V09-0104
Mount (Stirrup)
50mm
Howling beast in the centre.
Surface a little pitted.
£70 - £80

V09-0105
Mount (Stirrup)
50mm
Howling beast in the centre.
Even patina.
£80 - £100

V09-0106
Mount (Wolf's Head)
Stirrup
58mm
Possibly a stirrup terminal.
Encrusted iron on the surface.
Wolf type animal with its ears
pinned back. Rare.
£150 - £200

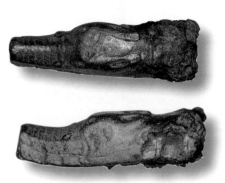

V09-0107
Mount (Stirrup)
Wolf's Head
40mm
Stirrup terminal. Traces of
iron on the surface.
£140 - £180

V09-0108
Stirrup Terminal
57mm
Stirrup terminal. Traces of
iron at the top.
£120 - £140

V09-0109
Mount (Stirrup)
43mm
Even patina. Appears to depict
a skeleton of an animal.
£70 - £80

V09-0110
Mount (Stirrup)
48mm
Surface rough and badly pitted.
£40 - £50

V09-0111
Mount (Stirrup)
42mm
Wolf's head design. Surface a
little rough.
£30 - £40

V09-0112
Mount (Stirrup)
45mm
Howling beast in the centre.
Surface a little uneven.
£60 - £70

V09-0113
Mount (Stirrup)
52mm
Smooth surface. Rich, even patina. Howling beast type.
£90 - £110

V09-0114
Mount (Stirrup)
50mm
Smooth surface. Even patina. Howling beast type.
£80 - £90

V09-0115
Mount (Stirrup)
52mm
Rough surface. Skeletal animal.
£25 - £30

V09-0116
Mount (Stirrup)
44mm
Face in the centre. One lug missing.
£25 - £30

V09-0201
Mount (Jellinge Style)
38mm
Interlace design in the Jellinge style. Dark even patina.
£75 - £100

V09-0202
Mount (Zoomorphic)
43mm
Two entwined beasts. Traces of silvering. Even patina.
£180 - £250

V09-0203
Mount (From a Book?)
58mm
Good detail and even patina. Beast with entwined serpent around its body. Very rare.
From £600

V09-0204
Mount (Zoomorphic)
61mm
Two entwined beasts. Surface
a little rough.
£300 - £350

V09-0205
Mount (Hinge-Like)
28mm
Face-like design. Possibly a
hinge from a casket.
£30 - £40

V09-0206
Mount (Bronze)
38mm
Bronze mount with traces of
gilding. Borre style.
£90 - £120

V09-0301
Mount (Bronze)
40mm
Interlaced design. Probably
two serpents. Even patina.
£120 - £150

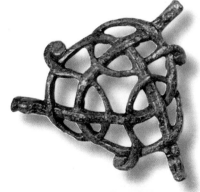

V10-0101
Bracelet (Silver)
67mm
Of typical style. Complete and
undamaged.
From £750

V10-0201
Bronze Ring (Gilded)
20mm dia
Surface a little ragged. Traces
of gilding.
£75 - £100

V10-0301
Gold Ring
18mm dia
Typical style. Circle
decoration across the bezel.
Twisted together under the
band. Rare in gold.
From £3,000

V11-0101
Statuette (Silver)
22mm
Helmeted figure maybe representing Thor. Left arm broken at the elbow. Rare.
£250 - £350

V12-0101
Strap-End (Beast with 8 Heads)
65mm
Good even patina. Ring and dot decoration.
£150 - £200

V12-0102
Strap-End (Face)
31mm
Dark patina. Undamaged. Chip-carved.
£50 - £60

V12-0103
Strap-End (Man Being Swallowed)
58mm
Surface a little rough. Depicts man being swallowed.
£120 - £150

V12-0104
Strap-End (Bronze)
33mm
Damaged. Patina flaking in places. Museum documented.
£100 - £120

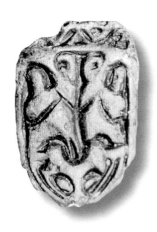

V12-0105
Strap-End
60mm
Lack of patination. Single rivet.
£70 - £80

V12-0201
Strap-End
56mm
Openwork design. Complete
and undamaged. Good even
patina.
£125 - £175

V12-0202
Strap-End
60mm
Open-work design. Even
patina. Small break along
one edge.
£120 - £150

V12-0203
Strap-End
51mm
Open-work design. Smooth
surface. Even, green patina.
£150 - £200

V12-0302
Buckle (Zoomorphic)
30mm
Entwined beasts. Pin missing.
£75 - £95

V12-0401
Buckle (With Plate)
90mm
Large buckle. Even colour,
Patina flaking in places. Rare.
£250 - £350

V15-0101
Strap-Junction
82mm
Four way strap junction.
Central boss rotates. Patina a
little patchy.
£100 - £150

V17-0101
Bronze Key
110mm
Suspension loop. Twisted shank. Even patina. Rare.
£300 - £400

V17-0102
Bronze Key
55mm
Complete and undamaged. Good even patina.
£90 - £125

V17-0103
Bronze Key
44mm
Suspension loop. A little damage. Even patina.
£70 - £95

V17-0104
Bronze Key
55mm
Suspension loop. Complete and undamaged. Good even patina.
£90 - £140

V17-0105
Bronze Key
55mm
Surface a little rough.
Cross hatch decoration
along the shaft.

£70 - £90

V17-0106
Bronze Key
88mm
Smooth surface.
Even patina. Small piece
broken off at one corner.

£120 - £150

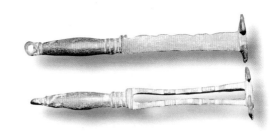

V17-0201
Iron Key
156mm
Good state of preservation.
Suspension loop.
Very large. Rare.

£130 - £160

V18-0101
Scales (Balance Arm)
76mm
Both balance arms present.
Pointer slightly bent. Even
patina.

£120 - £150

V18-0201
Weight (Bronze Iron
Filled)
26mm dia
Circular with two flat ends.
Decoration on both faces. Iron
bursting through the bronze.
Rare.
£80 - £100

V18-0202
Weight (Bronze)
15mm
Circular with two flat ends.
Decoration on both faces.
£60 - £70

V18-0301
Lead Weight
28mm dia
Centre contains part of a
gilded chip-carved brooch.
£100 - £150

V99-0101
Casket Handle
125mm
Patina a little patchy in places.
Two entwined beasts forming a
handle. Rare.
£150 - £200

THE NORMAN, MEDIEVAL AND TUDOR CENTURIES

The first six hundred years of the second millennium AD mark the transition from our ancient history to our modern society. The Norman invasion of 1066 heralded centuries containing the intertwined destinies of England and France framed by struggles for thrones; coloured by the blood of war, civil war, assassination and murder; cemented by royal marriages, family loyalties, treaties and dispensed law. Medieval feudalism came and went. Noble knights replaced warrior kings. Chivalry and honour prevailed - as did plague and poverty. The monarchy emerged as all powerful. Organised religion became even more organised before becoming disorganised to the point of religious persecution, just to accommodate a monarch's matrimonial difficulties.

These very changing times provide us with a wealth of artefacts of assorted type: religious, heraldic, trade, weaponry, horse trappings and, of course, personal items including jewellery. This is the literate age and this clearly shows in the amount of artefacts which bear engravings from medieval tournament spurs stating A true knight am I, Anger me and try to a Tudor posy ring asking one to Kepe promes. Very often the spelling will leave a lot to be desired. Engraved items are extremely popular amongst collectors and will attract a substantially higher price than an unengraved item of similar type. Also currently popular are religious artefacts which are numerous and include Limoges figure mounts, ampullae, pilgrim bottles, pilgrim badges, reliquary crosses, bible mounts and papal bullae.

This is an era to satisfy even the most ardent collector of rings. There are signet rings, posy rings, love-token rings, wedding rings, memorial rings, dress rings, fancy rings, stirrup rings, seal rings and rings bearing religious inscriptions. Nor are all rings for the finger for there are rings for the birds (hawk rings) as well as rings for the archer to assist in the pull of the bow-string. The collector of militaria is equally well catered for by items of armour, spurs, longbow bolts, arrowheads, sword and dagger pommels.

Those who are of a research loving nature need look no further than these medieval and Tudor times. From seal matrices to trade tokens, from heraldic devices on horse trappings to family crests on seal rings, there is much research material. And this research can be rewarding in all senses of the word for a well researched item will realise a much higher value.

M01-0101
Axe (Iron)
350mm
Large axe with maker's marks. Good state of preservation.
£200 - £300

M01-0102
Axehead (Iron)
160mm
As found condition.
£100 - £150

M02-0101
Arrowheads (Iron)
Longest 114mm
Various shapes and sizes.
From £25 each.

M02-0102
Arrowhead (Iron)
55mm
Barbed and tanged
(swallowtail) arrowhead.
Surface a little uneven.
£80 - £90

M02-0103
Arrowhead (Iron)
125mm
Barbed and tanged with a very
long socketed tang. Some
decoration. Rare type.
£100 - £120

M02-0201
Arrowhead (Bronze)
60mm
Even patina. Surface a little uneven.
£100 - £140

M03-0101
Iron Spear (Socketed)
260mm
Good state of preservation. Point intact.
£70 - £80

M03-0102
Iron Spear (With Gilding)
219mm
Surface a little uneven. Gold gilding on shaft. Rare.
£150 - £200

M04-0101
Iron Swords
980mm
Very rare to find complete.
From £3,000

M04-0102
Dagger (Iron)
365mm
Complete apart from its bone
or wooden handle. Good state
of preservation.
£800 - £900

M04-0103
Dagger (Bone Handle)
365mm
Complete with its handle and
crossguard. Chain mail
piercing blade.
£600 - £700

M04-0104
Dagger (With Pommel)
470mm
Bronze crossguard and
pommel. Iron blade.
Large size.
£800 - £900

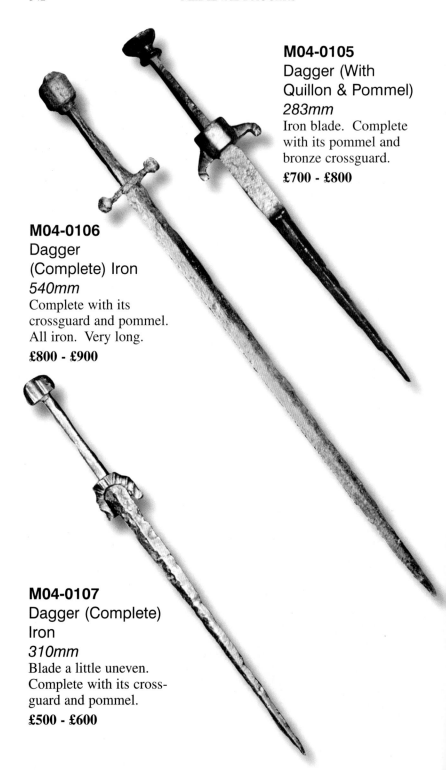

M04-0105
Dagger (With
Quillon & Pommel)
283mm
Iron blade. Complete
with its pommel and
bronze crossguard.
£700 - £800

M04-0106
Dagger
(Complete) Iron
540mm
Complete with its
crossguard and pommel.
All iron. Very long.
£800 - £900

M04-0107
Dagger (Complete)
Iron
310mm
Blade a little uneven.
Complete with its cross-
guard and pommel.
£500 - £600

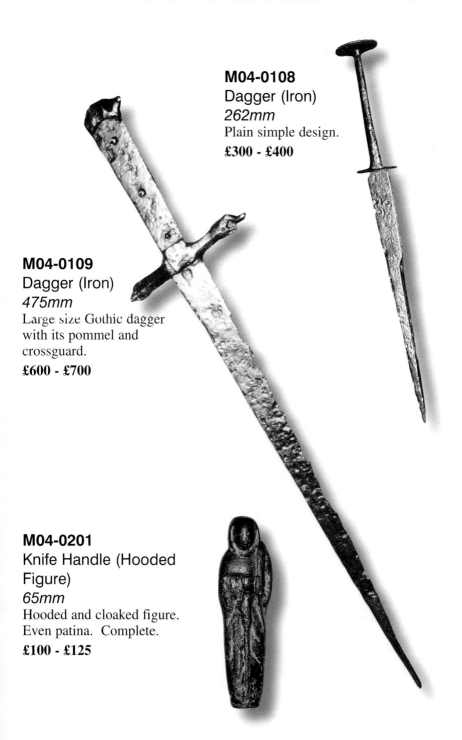

M04-0108
Dagger (Iron)
262mm
Plain simple design.
£300 - £400

M04-0109
Dagger (Iron)
475mm
Large size Gothic dagger
with its pommel and
crossguard.
£600 - £700

M04-0201
Knife Handle (Hooded
Figure)
65mm
Hooded and cloaked figure.
Even patina. Complete.
£100 - £125

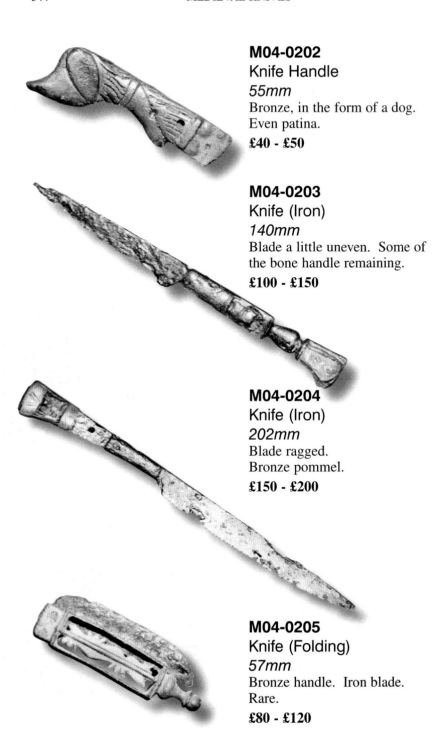

M04-0202
Knife Handle
55mm
Bronze, in the form of a dog.
Even patina.
£40 - £50

M04-0203
Knife (Iron)
140mm
Blade a little uneven. Some of
the bone handle remaining.
£100 - £150

M04-0204
Knife (Iron)
202mm
Blade ragged.
Bronze pommel.
£150 - £200

M04-0205
Knife (Folding)
57mm
Bronze handle. Iron blade.
Rare.
£80 - £120

M04-0301
Dagger Pommel
(Eagle's Head)
26mm
Sharp detail. Even patina.
£30 - £40

M04-0302
Dagger Pommel
32mm
Patina a little patchy.
Faceted sphere shape.
£40 - £50

M04-0303
Dagger Pommel
21mm
Bronze dog's head.
Even patina.
£15 - £20

M04-0304
Sword Pommel (Bronze)
58mm
Heavy bronze sword. Pommel decorated on both sides. Rare.
£180 - £225

M04-0305
Sword Pommel
40mm
Plain style. Even patina.
£60 - £70

M04-0306
Dagger Pommel
(Enamelled)
50mm
Traces of blue and white
enamel. Lozenge shape.
£200 - £250

M04-0307
Dagger Pommel
45mm
Engraved design of a crowned
lion. Smooth, even patina.
£150 - £200

M04-0308
Dagger Pommel
40mm
In the form of an expanding
cross with red and blue
enamel. Surface a little
uneven.
£150 - £200

M04-0309
Dagger Pommel
33mm
Quatrefoil shape with
cross design and
cross-hatching.
£30 - £40

M04-0310
Dagger Pommel
33mm
Resembling two birds'
heads.
Good, even patina.
£100 - £125

M04-0311
Dagger Pommel
35mm
Iron filled. Pellet
decoration.
£50 - £60

M04-0401
Dagger Quillon
('S' Shaped)
85mm
Light decoration.
Even patina. Complete.
£70 - £80

M04-0402
Quillon (For Dagger)
60mm
Even patina and complete.
£60 - £70

M04-0403
Dagger Quillon
(Decorated)
70mm
Decorated. No patination.
River find.
£70 - £80

M04-0501
Scabbard Chape
(Bronze)
55mm
Pierced design. Even patina.
£20 - £30

M04-0502
Chape (Bronze) Gilded
49mm
Gilding intact. Engraved detail
and initials.
£80 - £100

M04-0503
Dagger Chape
50mm
Decorated with cut-out
quatrefoil design.
£15 - £20

M04-0504
Scabbard (With Chape)
202mm
Decorated leather scabbard
with its chape. Rare.
£120 - £150

M04-0505
Scabbard Chape
60mm
Large chape from a
sword scabbard.
£40 - £50

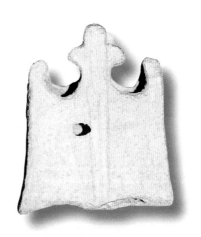

M04-0506
Dagger Chape (Silver)
35mm
Decorated on each facet. Rare.
£120 - £150

M05-0101
Mace Head (Bronze)
45mm
Even patina. Heavy and solid.
Rare.
£300 - £400

M05-0102
Mace Head (Iron)
278mm
Socketed with fins. Good state of preservation.
£150 - £200

M05-0201
Crossbow Bolt
(Iron) Socketed
80mm
Good state of preservation.
£35 - £40

M05-0202
Crossbow Bolt (Iron)
Tanged
108mm
Good state of preservation.
£35 - £40

M05-0203
Crossbow Bolts (Iron)
Longest 100mm
From £35 each

M05-0301
Archer's Ring
40mm
Incised decoration.
Even patina. Chunky.
£75 - £90

M05-0302
Archer's Ring
38mm
Even patina.
Thin construction.
£50 - £65

M05-0303
Archer's Ring
33mm
Light decoration.
Even patina.
£65 - £80

M05-0401
Sword Or Dagger
Hanger
60mm
Surface a little ragged.
Zoomorphic.
£60 - £70

M06-0101
Bronze Pin
100mm
Fairly plain style.
£20 - £30

M06-0102
Silver Pin (Gilded)
98mm
Filigree style decoration
on the head. Most of the
gilding remaining.
£70 - £80

M06-0103
Silver Pin (Gilded)
80mm
Filigree style decoration
on the head which is
fully gilded.
Undamaged.
£100 - £120

M06-0104
Silver Pin (Gilded)
70mm
Filigree style decoration
on the head which is
fully gilded.
Undamaged.
£90 - £110

M06-0105
Bronze Pin
70mm
Plain style.
Surface a little rough.
£15 - £20

M07-0101
Ring Brooch (Bronze)
25mm dia
Incised lines decoration.
Complete and undamaged.
£30 - £40

M07-0102
Ring Brooch (Bronze)
Hexagonal
22mm dia
Pelleted design. Complete.
Unusual shape.
£30 - £40

M07-0103
Ring Brooch (Bronze)
Clasped Hands
30mm
Smooth even patina. Single
turret. Complete.
£50 - £60

M07-0104
Ring Brooch (Bronze)
18mm dia
Smooth even patina. Two beasts eating each other's tails.
Complete. Small size.
£50 - £60

M07-0105
Ring Brooch (Bronze)
With Stones
17mm dia
Six turrets with stones.
Small size.
£30 - £40

M07-0106
Ring Brooch (Bronze)
With Turrets
30mm dia
Eight turrets.
Domino-like decoration.
£40 - £50

M07-0107
Ring Brooch (Bronze)
With Turrets
21mm dia
Six turrets. Even patina.
£35 - £45

M07-0108
Ring Brooch (Bronze)
With Turrets
33mm dia
Four turrets containing paste.
Smooth even patina.
£50 - £60

M07-0109
Ring Brooch (Gilded)
Bronze
26mm dia
Six turrets. Some gilding.
Complete.
£70 - £80

M07-0110
Ring Brooch (Bronze)
Gilded
17mm dia
Four knops on the ring and one on the pin. Corrosion in places.
£20 - £30

M07-0111
Ring Brooch (Enamelled)
13mm
Very small. Four joined crescents. Most of the enamel remaining.
£55 - £70

M07-0112
Ring Brooch (Bronze)
23mm
Six turrets with white paste.
£20 - £30

M07-0113
Ring Brooch (Bronze)
25mm dia
Slight traces of gilding.
Surface a little uneven.
With inscription.
£50 - £60

M07-0114
Ring Brooch (Two Heads)
61mm
Unusual double headed ring
brooch. Patina a little rough.
£80 - £90

M07-0115
Brooch (Two Animals)
39mm
Scarce type. Two beasts joined
by their rear and front feet.
£120 - £150

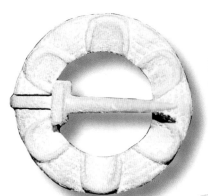

M07-0116
Ring Brooch (Gilded)
27mm
Traces of gilding. Decorated on
both surfaces.
£40 - £50

M07-0201
Ring Brooch (Silver)
21mm dia
Plain style. Complete.
£60 - £70

M07-0214
Ring Brooch (Gilded) Silver
16mm dia
Four beasts' heads. Gilded with
sharp detail. Rare.
£220 - £250

M07-0215
Ring Brooch (Gilded) Silver
18mm dia
Ring twisted and decorated.
Most gilding remains.
£90 - £110

M07-0216
Ring Brooch (Gilded) Silver
27mm
In the form of clasped hands.
Ring decorated.
£170 - £195

M07-0217
Ring Brooch (Silver)
Gilded
12mm dia
Four beasts' heads. Gilded.
Detail a little weak.
£90 - £110

M07-0218
Ring Brooch (Silver)
26mm
Decorated ring. Single knop
on the pin.
£80 - £100

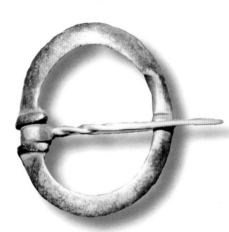

M07-0219
Annular Brooch (Silver)
23mm
Plain ring. Slight twist in
the pin.
£60 - £70

M07-0301
Ring Brooch (Gold)
25mm dia
Chain link style. Large size.
Rare.
£400 - £500

M08-0101
Pendant (Heraldic) Gilded
55mm
With hanger. 50% of the
gilding remaining.
£175 - £250

M08-0102
Pendant (With Hanger)
55mm
Enamelled griffin on the
hanger. Geometric design on
the pendant. Some gilding.
£80 - £100

M08-0103
Pendant (With Hanger)
46mm
50% of the gilding remaining.
£80 - £100

M08-0104
Pendant (With Hanger)
Acorn
36mm
Unusual style. Silvered of
which 50% remaining. Hanger
intact. Rare.
£80 - £100

M08-0105
Pendant (With Hanger)
70mm
Large size. Much of the enamel remaining. Silvered surface.
£100 - £125

M08-0106
Pendant (Gilded)
Enamelled
65mm
Dual pendant. Enamel intact.
Rare type.
£125 - £150

M08-0107
Pendant (Monkey) Gilded
50mm
Pendant with hanger bearing a
monkey-like head. most
gilding remaining.
£50 - £60

M08-0108
Pendant (Two Eagles)
Gilded
65mm
Unusual pendant with hanger.
Two opposite facing eagles.
Virtually all of the gilding
remains.
£125 - £150

M08-0109
Pendant (Chequered)
30mm
Shield shaped pendant with
traces of enamel.
£50 - £60

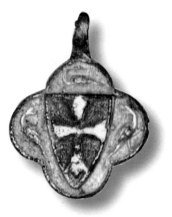

M08-0110
Pendant (Heraldic)
29mm
Quatrefoil shaped silvered pendant with cross in the centre
and three birds around. Red
enamel surrounds the cross.
£100 - £150

M08-0111
Pendant (Heraldic)
Enamelled
40mm
Quatrefoil shaped. Most of the
enamel remaining. Owl in the
centre.
£150 - £200

M08-0112
Pendant (Minstrel)
Enamelled
43mm
Quatrefoil shaped. Most of the
enamel remaining. Minstrel-
like figure in the centre. Rare.
£200 - £275

M08-0113
Pendant (Heraldic)
39mm
Some of the enamel remaining.
Lozenge shaped.
£75 - £95

M08-0114
Pendant (Crown)
Enamelled
28mm
Lozenge shaped. Most of the
enamel remaining. Small size.
£50 - £60

M08-0115
Pendant (Three Crowns)
35mm
Trefoil shaped. Traces of
enamel present.
£40 - £50

M08-0116
Pendant (Three Crowns)
Enamelled
44mm
Trefoil shaped. Most of the
enamel remaining. Large size.
£80 - £100

M08-0117
Pendant (Crowned Lion)
Enamelled
45mm
Shield shaped. Colourful
enamel. Crude style lion.
Rare.
£150 - £195

M08-0118
Pendant (Cross)
43mm
Traces of enamel remaining.
Shield shaped.
£70 - £90

M08-0119
Pendant (Cross)
Enamelled
39mm
Shield shaped. Full enamel
present.
£80 - £100

M08-0120
Pendant (Red Enamel)
35mm
Shield shaped. Surface a little
ragged.
Most enamel remaining.
£70 - £80

M08-0121
Pendant (Eagle)
Enamelled
44mm
Lozenge shaped. Most of the
enamel remaining.
£70 - £80

M08-0122
Pendant (Face)
Enamelled
38mm
Heavily gilded with full enamel. Face in the centre.
£140 - £160

M08-0123
Pendant (Lamb)
Enamelled
46mm
Quatrefoil shaped. Traces of
enamel. Sacrificial lamb.
£75 - £95

M08-0124
Pendant (Griffin)
Enamelled
43mm
Quatrefoil shaped. Much of
the enamel remaining. Griffin
in the centre.
£90 - £120

M08-0125
Harness Pendant (Griffin)
Enamelled
42mm
Lozenge shaped. Enamel
intact. Surface a little ragged.
£90 - £120

M08-0126
Pendant (Archer & Stag)
45mm
Quatrefoil shaped. Depicting
an archer pursuing a stag.
Enamel missing. Rare.
£90 - £120

M08-0127
Pendant (Chevrons)
Enamelled
40mm
Shield shaped. Much of the
enamel remaining.
£90 - £110

M08-0128
Pendant (Heraldic)
Enamelled
48mm
Shield shaped.
Enamel virtually intact.
£100 - £140

M08-0129
Pendant (Heraldic) Three
Lions
49mm
Shield shaped. Traces of
enamel.
£70 - £90

M08-0130
Pendant (Castle)
36mm
Castle or priory in the centre.
£70 - £90

M08-0131
Pendant (Gilded)
35mm
Interlaced design.
£35 - £45

M08-0132
Pendant
44mm
Traces of enamel. Large size.
£60 - £80

M08-0133
Harness Pendant
35mm
Much of the enamel remaining.
£50 - £60

M08-0134
Harness Pendant
(Winged Beast)
40mm dia
Some enamel remaining.
Large size.
£80 - £100

M08-0135
Pendant (Lion)
25mm
Square shaped. Small size.
£25 - £35

M08-0136
Pendant (Ring & Dot)
Gilded
40mm
Square shaped. 50% of the
gilding remaining.
£25 - £35

M08-0137
Pendant (Cross Hatching)
40mm
Square shaped. Surface quite
rough.
£25 - £30

M08-0138
Pendant (Gilded)
65mm
Shield shaped. Letter "M" in
the centre. Quatrefoil
decoration around the edge.
Large size.
Suspension loop missing.
£90 - £100

M08-0139
Pendant (Heraldic)
Enamelled
47mm
Lozenge shaped. Enamel
intact. Suspension loop
missing.
£90 - £100

M08-0140
Pendant (Heraldic)
30mm
Traces of enamel.
Suspension loop intact.
£90 - £130

M08-0141
Pendant (Gilded)
With Hanger
96mm
Large pendant with its hanger.
Much of the gilding remaining.
£90 - £110

M08-0142
Pendant (Lis) Gilded
With Hanger
69mm
Heavily gilded. With its
original hanger
£40 - £50

M08-0143
Pendant (Heraldic)
66mm
With hanger. Surface a little
uneven. Most enamel missing.
£120 - £150

M08-0144
Pendant (Peacock)
62mm
Gilded surface. Enamelled
peacock.
£100 - £120

M08-0145
Pendant (With Hanger)
50mm
With its hanger and most of its enamel.

£130 - £160

M08-0146
Pendant (With Hanger)
62mm
With hanger. White enamelled owl.

£120 - £150

M08-0147
Harness Pendant
(With Hanger)
56mm
Heraldic with all enamel and most gilding remaining.

£175 - £225

M08-0148
Harness Pendant (Butterfly)
54mm
With hanger. Lozenge shaped.
Enamel intact.
£120 - £150

M08-0149
Pendant (Heraldic)
57mm
With hanger. Traces of gilding.
£130 - £160

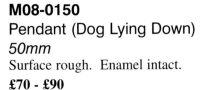

M08-0150
Pendant (Dog Lying Down)
50mm
Surface rough. Enamel intact.
£70 - £90

M08-0151
Pendant (With Hanger)
56mm
With hanger. Most of the enamel
remaining.
£120 - £150

M08-0152
Pendant (Heraldic)
45mm
With hanger. Full enamel. Arms
of William of Harpendene.
£150 - £195

M08-0153
Pendant (Butterfly)
60mm
With hanger and most enamel.
£120 - £150

M08-0154
Pendant
29mm
Surface a little rough. Four stars and crescent.
£60 - £70

M08-0155
Pendant (Heraldic)
42mm
Surface a little rough. Blue enamel still remains.
£70 - £95

M08-0156
Pendant (Stork)
46mm
Surface a little rough. Most of the blue enamel remains.
£70 - £90

M08-0157
Pendant (Dodo) Enamelled
46mm
Surface rough. Lozenge shape.
Most enamel remains.
£120 - £150

M08-0158
Pendant (Heraldic)
45mm
Surface a little rough. Red and
blue enamel remaining.
£120 - £150

M08-0159
Harness Pendant
45mm
Surface rough.
Enamelled unicorn.
£80 - £110

M08-0160
Pendant (Enamelled)
42mm
Most enamel remaining. Rare crossed key and dagger design.
£140 - £175

M08-0161
Pendant (Lion)
22mm
Large and impressive. Rampant lion.
£150 - £175

M08-0162
Pendant (Stud Suspension)
64mm
Large, unusual pendant. Three poppies or flowers in red. Gilding around.
£175 - £250

M08-0163
Pendant (Enamelled)
Flower
25mm
Most of the enamel and gilding
remaining.
£70 - £90

M08-0164
Pendant (Heraldic)
46mm
Surface rough. Blue enamelled
rampant lion.
£110 - £140

M08-0165
Pendant (Gilded)
Enamelled
60mm
Large quatrefoil pendant.
Approximately half of the enamel
and gilding remaining.
£150 - £175

M08-0166
Harness Pendant
45mm
Surface rough. White enamelled
sleeping dog.
£70 - £80

M08-0167
Pendant (Enamelled)
44mm
Strong detail. Enamelled dog in a
lying position.
£80 - £100

M08-0168
Pendant (Heraldic)
44mm
Virtually all enamel and gilding
present. Rare.
£250 - £300

M08-0169
Pendant (Heraldic)
39mm
Surface a little rough.
£80 - £90

M08-0170
Pendant (Heraldic)
42mm
Traces of gilding. Enamel
missing. Umfraville family.
£130 - £160

M08-0171
Pendant (Three Crowns)
43mm
Surface a little rough.
Three crowns.
£70 - £80

M08-0172
Pendant (Hawk)
33mm
Unusual pendant depicting a
hawk, an arm and a ring brooch.
£150 - £175

M08-0173
Harness Pendant
42mm
Raised, gilded cross on a plain
background.
£60 - £70

M08-0174
Harness Pendant
56mm
Large pendant. Traces of gilding.
£20 - £30

M08-0175
Harness Pendant
41mm
Shield within a square over
a quatrefoil. Heavily gilded.
£150 - £175

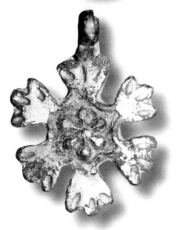

M08-0176
Harness Pendant
43mm
Blue enamel and silvered
surfaces.
£60 - £70

M08-0177
Pendant (Eagle)
31mm
Eagle with head facing left.
Traces of gilding.
£50 - £60

M08-0178
Pendant (Gilded) With Bell
47mm
Unusual style with a bell
suspended in the centre.
£40 - £50

M08-0179
Harness Pendant (Letter 'T')
59mm
Large pendant heavily gilded with
the letter "T" in the centre.
£120 - £150

M08-0180
Pendant (Tau Cross)
39mm
Suspension loop broken. Gilded
tau cross with cross hatch design.
£80 - £100

M08-0181
Pendant (Silver) Amethyst
23mm
Large amethyst set in a silver
surround.
£200 - £250

M09-0101
Heraldic Penant
(Enamelled) mount
48mm
Patina a little patchy. Most of
the enamel remaining. Scarce.
£100 - £125

M09-0102
Mount (Enamelled)
40mm
Lozenge shaped. Fairly plain.
All of the blue enamel
remaining.
£35 - £45

M09-0103
Mount (Enamelled)
27mm
Shield shaped. Some enamel
remaining. Surface a little
uneven.
£80 - £100

M09-0104
Mount (Hcraldic)
Enamelled
35mm
Shield shaped. Some enamel
remaining. Traces of gilding.
£35 - £45

M09-0105
Mount (Trefoil) Enamelled
45mm
Trefoil shaped. Traces of
enamel. Large.
£40 - £50

M09-0106
Mount (Bird) Enamelled
35mm
Most of the enamel remaining.
£50 - £70

M09-0106 (A)
Mount (Stud) Heraldic
19mm
Shield shaped. Most of the
enamel remaining. Chequered
design. Small.
£20 - £25

M09-0107
Mount (Enamelled)
60mm
Most of the enamel remaining.
Good detail of a lady crowning
her knight. Rare.
£800 - £900

M09-0108
Mount (Enamelled)
44mm
Rectangular shape.
Traces of gilding.
£60 - £70

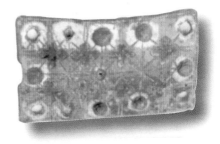

M09-0109
Mount (Enamelled)
45mm
Square shaped. Most of the
enamel remaining.
£75 - £100

M09-0110
Mount (Three Lions)
Enamelled
40mm
Shield shaped. Most of the
enamel remaining.
£70 - £100

M09-0111
Mount (Lion of St Mark)
45mm
Traces of red, blue, green and white enamel and traces of gilding.
£250 - £300

M09-0112
Mount (Letter W)
57mm
Surface a little rough. Letter "W" in the centre.
£50 - £60

M09-0113
Mount
39mm
Unusual depiction of a crowned winged beast with a human head.
£120 - £150

M09-0114
Mount (Stud)
18mm
Blue enamel and gilding.
Small size.
£50 - £60

M09-0115
Mount (Heraldic)
32mm
Chequered shield.
Surface a little rough.
£70 - £80

M09-0116
Mount (Heraldic)
46mm
Large heraldic mount. Rampant
lion. Red enamelled background.
£160 - £200

M09-0117
Mount (Heraldic)
18mm
Small heraldic stud.
Surface a little rough.
£30 - £40

M09-0118
Mount (Heraldic)
49mm
Three gilded lions.
Red enamelled background,
most remaining.
£175 - £225

M09-0119
Mount (Gold Inlay)
60mm
Large heraldic mount
with gold inlay.
£150 - £200

M09-0120
Mount (Gilded)
23mm
Small gilded stud.
£40 - £50

M09-0121
Mount (Heraldic)
17mm
Shield within a quatrefoil.
Gilded and enamelled.
£40 - £50

M09-0122
Mount (Enamelled)
34mm
Cloisonne type inlay.
£120 - £150

M09-0123
Mount (Bird) Enamelled
40mm
Fully gilded.
Traces of red enamel.
£160 - £200

M09-0124
Mount (Enamelled)
54mm
Mount probably from a
casket.
Blue enamel and gilding.
£60 - £75

M09-0125
Mount (Enamelled)
30mm
Most of the enamel
remaining.
£70 - £80

M09-0201
Mount (Silver) Gilded
16mm
Square shaped. Loop at the back. Most of the gilding remaining.
£70 - £80

M09-0202
Mount (Two Beasts)
44mm
Two protruding heads. Pierced for mounting.
£80 - £100

M09-0203
Mount (Zoomorphic)
35mm
Even patina. Beast with its tongue sticking out.
£60 - £70

M09-0204
Mount (Gilded) Bronze
60mm
Face in the centre with design around. Most of the gilding remaining.
£125 - £150

M09-0205
Mount (Beast)
65mm
Beast with its foot in its mouth. Surface a little ragged.
£100 - £125

M09-0206
Mount (Rampant Lion)
50mm
Openwork design. Good even patina. Complete. Rare.
£250 - £300

M09-0207
Mount (Gilded Dog)
32mm
Three dimensional. Most of the gilding remaining. Good detail.
£125 - £150

M09-0208
Mount (Gilded) Bronze
28mm
Openwork design. Small size.
£60 - £70

M09-0209
Mount (Pewter) Lis
55mm
Shield shaped. Lis in the
centre. Openwork design.
£50 - £60

M09-0210
Mount (Ecclesiastical)
Bronze
55mm
Design comprising openwork
triangles. Even patina.
£80 - £100

M09-0211
Mount (Bronze) With
Inscription
55mm
Lettering on one side.
Floral design on the other.
£25 - £30

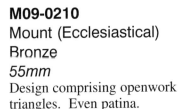

M09-0212
Mount (Bronze) With
Inscription
85mm
Thin strip with rivets at each end.
£25 - £30

M09-0213
Mount (Roundel) Bronze
62mm dia
Two figures either side of an altar with banners above. Creased down the centre.

£175 - £200

M09-0214
Mount (Roundel)
59mm dia
Two angels either side of a shield.

£175 - £225

M09-0215
Mount (Roundel) Bronze
40mm
Crowned key in the centre. Traces of enamel.

£100 - £120

M09-0216
Mount (Ecclesiastical)
47mm
Even patina. Design of
openwork triangles.
£80 - £100

M09-0217
Mount (Ecclesiastical)
62mm
Surface a little rough.
Openwork design.
£60 - £80

M09-0218
Mount (Silver)
37mm
Decorated with niello inlay.
£60 - £70

M09-0219
Mount (Gilded)
29mm
Most gilding remains.
Depicting winged beast
in a crouched position.
£80 - £100

M09-0220
Mount
28mm
Cross in the centre. Good,
even patina.
£20 - £30

M09-0221
Mount (Beasts)
34mm
Three beasts' heads overlying
a triangle.
£80 - £100

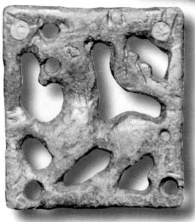

M09-0222
Mount (Rampant Lion)
23mm
Openwork design. Even
patination.
£70 - £80

M09-0223
Mount (Dog)
34mm
Surface a little patchy.
£15 - £20

M09-0224
Mount (Lion)
30mm
Openwork design.
Three dimensional.
£70 - £80

M09-0225
Mount (Lion)
23mm
Openwork design. Three
dimensional. Slight damage.
£60 - £70

M10-0101
Bronze Ring (Anchor)
20mm dia
Good even patina. Unusual device
(anchor) on the bezel.
£90 - £110

M10-0102
Bronze Ring (Crowned T)
19mm dia
Even patina. Small size.
£80 - £90

M10-0103
Bronze Ring (Letter P)
22mm dia
A little pitted on the surface.
Large size.
£75 - £85

M10-0104
Bronze Ring (Crowned T.I)
24mm dia
Good even patina. Unusual. Two
entwined letters. Very large size.
£100 - £125

M10-0105
Bronze Ring (Hand and Sword)
23mm dia
Good even patina. Unusual.
Hand and sword on the bezel.
Large size.
£100 - £120

M10-0106
Bronze Ring
19mm dia
Engraved motif on bezel.
Two serpents' heads forming
the shank.
£80 - £90

M10-0107
Bronze Ring (Letter I)
20mm dia
Round bezel. Engraved
decoration. Maybe a letter "I".
Even patina.
£80 - £90

M10-0108
Bronze Ring (Letter P)
22mm dia
Good even patina. Large size.
£80 - £90

M10-0109
Bronze Ring (Letter W)
21mm dia
Surface a little uneven. Crude style.
£60 - £70

M10-0110
Bronze Ring (Letter W)
22mm dia
Surface a little ragged. Simple style.
£40 - £50

M10-0111
Bronze Ring (Letter A)
20mm dia
Surface a little uneven. Simple style.
£60 - £70

M10-0112
Bronze Ring (Letter R)
24mm dia
Good even patina. Sharp detail. Very large size.
£100 - £125

M10-0113
Bronze Ring (Crowned RI)
21mm dia
Unusual spiral shape band. Sharp detail. Even patina.
£110 - £130

M10-0114
Bronze Ring (Crowned I)
21mm dia
A little mis-shapen. Uneven
surface.
£40 - £50

M10-0115
Bronze Ring (Saint)
18mm dia
Unusual figure of a saint on
the bezel. Good smooth surface with even patina.
£120 - £140

M10-0116
Bronze Ring (Letter R)
28mm dia
Even patina.
£100 - £125

M10-0117
Bronze Ring (Letter R)
28mm dia
Even patina.
£100 - £125

M10-0118
Bronze Ring
(Crowned M)
22mm
Surface a little
uneven. Large size.
£80 - £90

M10-0119
Bronze Ring
(Castle)
20mm
Smooth surface.
Traces of gilding.
Castle on the bezel.
£90 - £100

M10-0201
Silver Ring (Lis)
22mm dia
Good silver.
£175 - £225

M10-0202
Silver Ring (Letter M)
19mm dia
Crude style.
£150 - £160

M10-0203
Silver Ring (Letter T)
21mm dia
Good silver.
£175 - £200

M10-0204
Silver Ring (Four Bezels)
19mm dia
Devices engraved on each of
the four bezels. Good silver.
Small size.

£150 - £200

M10-0205
Silver Ring
(Iconographic)
19mm dia
Figure of a saint on the bezel.
Spiral design on the band.

£200 - £225

M10-0206
Silver Ring (Inscription)
22mm dia
Good silver. Wearable size.
Inscription on bezel.
£200 - £250

M10-0207
Silver Ring (Gilded) With
Inscription
22mm dia
Thin band. 50% of the gilding
remains. Large size.
£150 - £200

M10-0208
Silver Ring (Gilded)
Inscription
21mm dia
Most of the gilding remaining.
Decorated band. Sharp detail.
Undamaged. Wearable
size.
£250 - £300

M10-0209
Silver Ring (Gilded)
22mm dia
Most of the gilding remaining.
Heart in the centre of the bezel
with petal design each
side.
£250 - £300

M10-0210
Silver Ring (Gilded)
20mm dia
Much of the gilding remaining.
Two bezels, one depicting a
crowned heart, the other
clasped hands. Complete and
undamaged.
£400 - £450

M10-0211
Silver Ring (Gilded)
19mm dia
Much of the gilding remaining.
Crowned hands clutching a
heart form the bezel.
Openwork band. Complete and
undamaged.
£350 - £400

M10-0212
Silver Ring (Gilded)
17mm dia
Tudor rose bezel.
Enamel missing.
Some gilding remaining.
£175 - £225

M10-0213
Silver Ring (Gilded) With Inscription
23mm dia
Unusual style. Much of the gilding remaining. Large size.
£250 - £300

M10-0214
Silver Ring (Iconographic) Gilded
22mm dia
Two saints on the bezel. Two shields either side. Most of the gilding remaining.
Decorated band. Large size.
£600 - £700

M10-0215
Silver Ring (Iconographic) Gilded
19mm dia
Two saints on the bezel. Flower design on the shank. Some gilding remaining. Small size.
£350 - £450

M10-0216
Silver Ring (Gilded) With Stone
21mm dia
Blue sapphire stone. Most of the gilding missing. Wearable size.

£125 - £150

M10-0217
Silver Ring (Bead Bezel)
20mm dia
Unusual style. Ancient bead in the centre of the bezel. Good silver.

£200 - £250

M10-0218
Silver Ring (Norman)
18mm
Decorated band.
Slightly raised bezel.

£170 - £190

M10-0219
Silver Ring (With Niello)
21mm
Decorated band. Niello inlay.
Good condition.
£180 - £220

M10-0220
Silver Ring
(With Inscription)
18mm
Posy ring. Decorated band.
Inscription on the inside.
£170 - £200

M10-0221
Silver Ring (Gilded)
18mm
Clasped hands. Decorated band.
Gold gilded.
£150 - £200

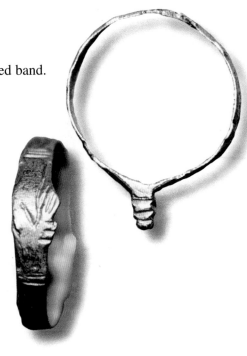

M10-0222
Silver Ring (Gilded)
21mm
Fully gilded. Two bezels, one
depicting a crowned heart, the
other clasped hands.
£425 - £475

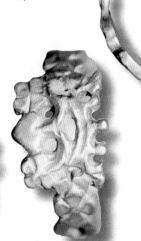

M10-0223
Silver Ring (Gilded)
22mm
Gold gilded. Large size.
Merchant's marks engraved in the
bezel.
£300 - £350

M10-0224
Ring (Silver)
19mm int dia
Traces of gilding. Crude rose
design on the bezel.
£120 - £150

M10-0225
Ring (Silver) Gilded
20mm dia
Band formed of two twists.
Rose design bezel.
£130 - £160

M10-0226
Silver Ring (Gilded)
With Stone
19mm int dia
Double inscription on the outside.
Two beasts' heads holding the
bezel. Set with a garnet. Rare
type.
£500 - £600

M10-0227
Silver Ring (Gilded)
With Stone
19mm
Most gilding remaining.
Bezel a little damaged. Pretty
amethyst setting.
£300 - £350

M10-0228
Silver Ring (Gilded)
20mm dia
Large size. Decorated all around
the band and bezel.
£250 - £300

M10-0229
Silver Ring (Inscription)
Gilded
22mm dia
Fully gilded. Inscription on the
bezel. Large size.

£500 - £600

M10-0230
Silver Ring (Iconographic)
18mm dia
Saint on the bezel. Flower design
on the shank. Small size.

£350 - £400

M10-0231
Silver Ring (Iconographic)
20mm dia
Surface a little ragged. Weak detail.
£175 - £195

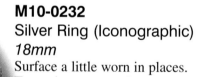

M10-0232
Silver Ring (Iconographic)
18mm
Surface a little worn in places. Two saints engraved.
£200 - £250

M10-0301
Gold Ring (Stirrup
Shape) With Stone
23mm dia
Large wearable size.
Undamaged. Original perfect
stone.
From £1,000

M10-0302
Gold Ring (Stirrup
Shape) Turquoise Stone
20mm dia
Slightly mis-shapen. Small
size. Original perfect stone.
From £750

M10-0303
Gold Ring (Garnet)
25mm dia
Large original garnet.
Complete and undamaged.
Wearable size.
From £1,000

M10-0304
Gold Ring (Amethyst)
15mm dia
Small size. Unusual style
bezel. Original stone.
£600 - £700

M10-0305
Gold Ring (Turquoise)
19mm dia
Stirrup style. Original stone.
Undamaged. Small size.
£650 - £750

M10-0306
Gold Ring (Rock Crystal)
16mm dia
Black and white enamel. Very
small size. Rock crystal stone.
£750 - £850

M10-0307
Gold Ring
(Stirrup Shape)
21mm dia
Plain band. Claw style bezel
holding a turquoise stone.
£400 - £500

M10-0308
Gold Ring (Decorated)
16mm dia
Hollow construction. Enamel
missing. Small size.
£250 - £350

M10-0309
Gold Ring (Posy)
Enamelled
18mm dia
Much of the enamel remaining.
Inscription on the inside. Rare.
£350 - £450

M10-0310
Gold Ring (Horse Hoof)
22mm dia
Seal ring. Chevron design on
the shank. Undamaged and
attributable to a family.
Rare.
From £3,000

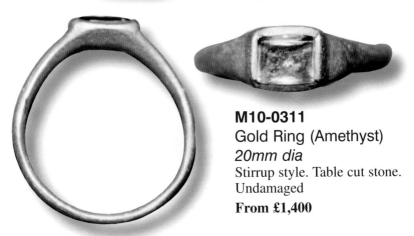

M10-0311
Gold Ring (Amethyst)
20mm dia
Stirrup style. Table cut stone.
Undamaged
From £1,400

M10-0312
Gold Ring (Blue Sapphire)
20mm dia
Faceted bezel and stone.
Undamaged
From £1,300

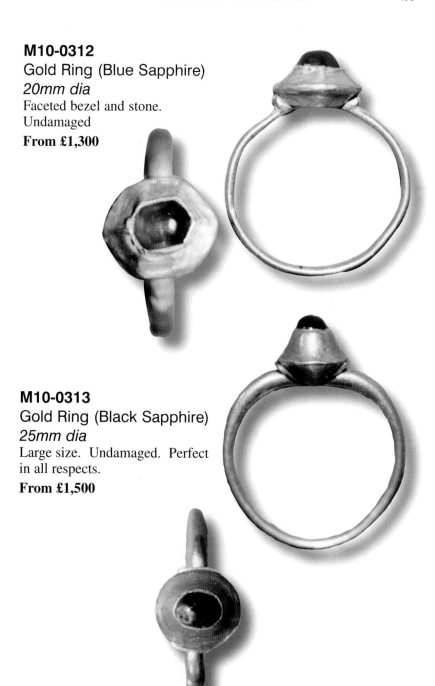

M10-0313
Gold Ring (Black Sapphire)
25mm dia
Large size. Undamaged. Perfect
in all respects.
From £1,500

M10-0314
Gold Ring (Amethyst)
21mm dia
A little mis-shapen. Uneven
bezel.
£900 - £1,200

M10-0315
Gold Ring
22mm dia
Decorated band. Large size. A
little uneven around the stone.
From £1,100

M10-0316
Gold Ring (Sapphire)
23mm
Large size. A little mis-shapen
around the stone setting.

From £900

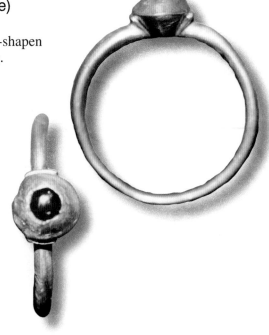

M10-0317
Gold Ring (Sapphire)
19mm
Small ring. Some damage
around the bezel.

From £900

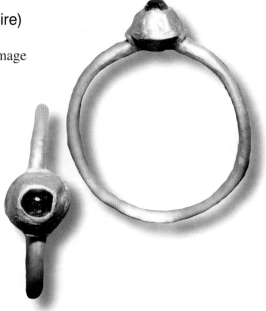

M10-0318
Gold Ring (Garnet)
17mm dia
Small size. Decorated band.
Pretty garnet setting.
£900 - £1,100

M10-0319
Gold Ring (Inscription)
Blue Sapphire
22mm dia
Large size. Inscription around
the outside of the band.
From £1,400

M10-0320
Gold Ring (Emerald)
18mm
Thin band. Rectangular bezel set with an emerald. Stone damaged.
£700 - £800

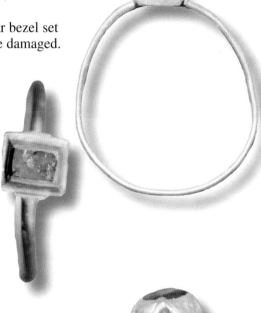

M10-0321
Gold Ring (Amethyst)
20mm dia
Traces of black enamel on the shoulders. Petal design bezel.
From £1,000

M10-0322
Gold Ring (Amethyst & Sapphires)
18mm
Unusual style. Heart shaped amethyst in the bezel. Stones set from underneath.

From £1,500

M10-0323
Gold Ring (Turquoise)
20mm
Large bezel with turquoise setting surrounded by rock crystals.

£900 - £1,000

M10-0324
Gold Ring (Rock Crystal)
21mm
Traces of black enamel. Large rock crystal in the centre flanked by three rock crystals on either side.

£800 - £900

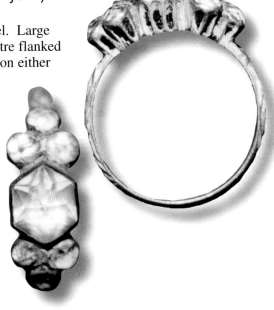

M10-0325
Gold Ring (Mermaid)
With Inscription
15mm dia
Inscription on the inside. Mermaid curved backwards forming the bezel.
Rare.

£1,100 - £1,300

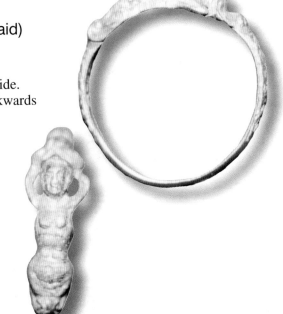

M10-0326
Gold Ring (Flower)
15mm
Small size. Flower engraved on
the bezel. Possibly saffron plant.
£300 - £400

M10-0327
Gold Ring (Skull)
19mm
Thin band. Small bezel of a
skull. Black enamel inlaid.
Decorated shoulders.
£400 - £500

M10-0328
Gold Iconographic Ring
(With Inscription)
20mm dia
Good size. One saint engraved
on the bezel. Inscription inside
the band.
From £3,000

M10-0329
Gold Ring (Three Saints)
20mm
Three saints, each one forming a
separate bezel. Decorated
between each bezel. Perfect and
rare.
From £5,000

M11-0101
Crucifix (Gilded)
57mm
Some gilding remaining.
Letters engraved on each arm.
£125 - £150

M11-0102
Crucifix (Gilded) Silver
50mm
Suspension loops at the top
and bottom. Most of the gilding remaining.
£250 - £350

M11-0103
Crucifix Figure (Bronze)
75mm
Good detail. Undamaged.
Even patina.
£150 - £175

M11-0104
Figure of a Saint (Bronze)
62mm
Enamel remaining on the face
but missing from the body.
£150 - £200

M11-0105
Figure of a Saint (Bronze)
55mm
Fairly ragged surface. Weak
detail.
£35 - £45

M11-0106
Figure of a Saint (Bronze)
70mm
Weak detail. Surface a little
uneven. Large size.
£70 - £80

M11-0107
Figure of a Saint (Gilded)
Bronze
58mm
Gilding and enamel all intact.
Glass eyes in place.
£600 - £700

M11-0108
Figure of a Saint (Gilded)
Bronze
62mm
Gilding and enamel all intact.
Glass eyes in place.
£650 - £800

M11-0109
Crowned Head (Gilded)
Bronze
38mm
Traces of gilding. Clear detail.
£80 - £100

M11-0110
Mount (Limoges)
55mm
Surface a little rough.
Damaged in places.
£75 - £95

M11-0111
Bronze Head (Mount)
35mm
Head of a lady. Rough surface.
£50 - £60

M11-0112
Crucifix
54mm
Surface a little rough. Damaged
in places.
£50 - £70

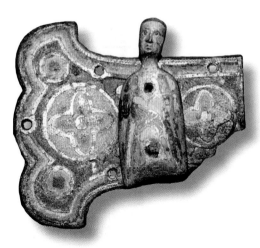

M11-0113
Arm From Cross
(With Figure of Saint)
85mm
Virtually full enamel and gilding. Figure probably represents St. John. Very rare.
From £1,300

M12-0101
Strap-End
(Decorated)
85mm
Smooth even patina. Plain style.
£20 - £30

M12-0102
Strap-End
(Acorn Top)
102mm
Lacking patina. Large size.
£60 - £70

M12-0103
Bronze Strap-End
(Head)
45mm
Even patina. Complete.
£50 - £60

M12-0104
Strap-End (With Ear Scoop)
55mm
Beast with a long tongue forming an ear scoop. Rare.
£70 - £80

M12-0105
Strap-End (Bird)
58mm
Smooth even patina. Good style. Complete.
£90 - £100

M12-0106
Strap-End (Lettering)
56mm
Letters engraved on the surface. Foliate design. Even patina.
£60 - £70

M12-0107
Strap-End (Eagle)
60mm
Eagle in the centre. Good even patina.
£125 - £150

M12-0108
Strap-End (Bronze)
Letter 'R'
70mm
Letter "R" on the plate.
Even patina. Traces of
silvering. Large size.
£125 - £150

M12-0109
Bronze Strap-End
(St Christopher)
90mm
St. Christopher in the
centre. Traces of
silvering. Complete and
undamaged. Rare.
£200 - £250

M12-0110
Strap-End (Letter M)
90mm
Patina ragged and patchy.
Large size.
£60 - £70

M12-0111
Strap-End (St Christopher)
60mm
Complete and undamaged.
Silvered surface. Rare.
£200 - £250

M12-0112
Strap-End (From a Book)
110mm
Patina uneven. Surface a little dented.
£80 - £100

M12-0113
Strap-End (Gilded)
Inscribed
65mm
50% of gilding remaining.
Undamaged.
£125 - £150

M12-0114
Strap-End (Silver)
Inscribed
70mm
Much of the gilding remaining.
Complete.
£200 - £250

M12-0115
Strap-End (Man)
48mm
Even patina Good detail.
Scarce type.
£90 - £100

M12-0116
Strap-End (Gilded)
Inscribed
65mm
Most gilding remaining.
Engraved. Undamaged.
£125 - £150

M12-0117
Strap-End (Gilded)
Inscribed
40mm
Surface a little rough. Some
gilding remaining. Engraved.
£40 - £50

M12-0118
Strap-End (From A Book)
78mm
Traces of gilding. Patina
uneven.
£80 - £90

M12-0119
Bronze Strap-End
90mm
See M12-0109 for similar example. This one has figure missing from the centre.
£50 - £60

M12-0120
Strap-End
57mm
Same as M12-0106 but without the inscription.
£30 - £40

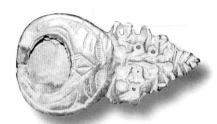

M12-0121
Strap-End
65mm
Silvered surface. Plain style.
£25 - £30

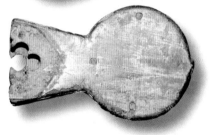

M12-0122
Strap-End
50mm
Crowned head. Surface a little uneven.
£50 - £60

M12-0123
Strap-End
60mm
Acorn knop end. Even patina.
£20 - £30

M12-0124
Strap-End
62mm
Acorn knop end. Some decoration on the plate. Good, even patina.
£40 - £50

M12-0125
Strap-End (Glass Eyes)
28mm
Unusual style. Beast with its mouth open. Glass beads set in the eyes.
£90 - £120

M12-0201
Buckle (Hand & Arm)
55mm
Even patina. Complete and undamaged.
£25 - £30

M12-0202
Locking Buckle
30mm
Even patina. Working order.
£30 - £40

M12-0203
Buckle
40mm
Patina a little ragged.
£15 - £20

M12-0204
Buckle (Two Figures)
65mm
Two figures standing on a lion
with their hands on each
other's head. Patina a little
patchy. Very rare.
£175 - £225

M12-0205
Buckle (Beasts)
32mm
Traces of gilding. Two beasts
facing each other. Smooth even
surface.
£120 - £150

M12-0206
Buckle
30mm
Beast biting its tail. Patina a little
patchy.
£80 - £100

M12-0207
Buckle
30mm
Beast biting its tail.
Good detail. Smooth,
even patina.
£140 - £170

M12-0208
Buckle (Crowned Head)
28mm
Smooth, even surface.
Small size.
£30 - £40

M12-0209
Buckle (Crowned Head)
38mm
Surface a little uneven.
Good size.
£35 - £45

M12-0210
Buckle (Face)
29mm
Surface a little pitted.
Small size.
£25 - £30

M12-0211
Buckle
30mm
Surface a little uneven.
£10 - £15

M12-0212
Buckle
28mm
Good colour. Smooth,
even patina.
£30 - £40

M12-0213
Buckle (Head)
18mm
Patina a little patchy.
Small size.
£10 - £15

M12-0214
Buckle
58mm
Patina a little ragged.
Damage in places.
£30 - £40

M12-0215
Buckle (Bird)
49mm
Buckle in the form of a bird.
With its pin.
£40 - £50

M12-0301
Buckle Plate (Lion)
40mm
Openwork design.
Even patina.
£80 - £90

M12-0302
Buckle Plate (Lion)
30mm
Openwork design.
Even patina.
£70 - £80

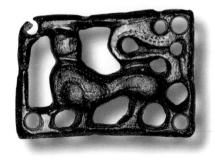

M12-0303
Buckle Plate (Two
Beasts) Gilded
35mm
Traces of gilding.
Surface a little ragged.
£60 - £70

M12-0304
Buckle Plate (Dog)
58mm
Openwork design.
Detail fairly worn.
£80 - £90

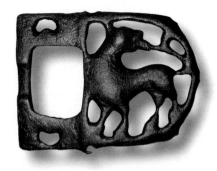

M12-0305
Buckle Plate (Dog)
60mm
Openwork design.
Even patina. Good detail.
Some damage.
£125 - £150

M12-0306
Buckle Plate
40mm
Figure playing a harp. With
inscription. Silvered surface.
£60 - £70

M12-0307
Buckle Plate (Limoges)
31mm
Enamel intact but surface a little ragged.
£65 - £75

M12-0401
Buckle (With Plate)
Gilded
54mm
50% of gilding remaining.
Complete.
£80 - £90

M12-0402
Buckle (With Plate) Beast
45mm
50% of gilding remaining.
Complete.
£80 - £90

M12-0403
Buckle (With Plate)
35mm
Basic design. Even patina.
£15 - £20

M12-0404
Buckle (With Plate)
45mm
Basic design. Even patina.
£15 - £20

M12-0405
Buckle (With Plate)
45mm
Basic design. Patchy patina.
£10 - £15

M12-0406
Buckle (With Plate)
Zoomorphic
65mm
Buckle in the form of a beast.
Dark, even patina.
£70 - £90

M12-0407
Buckle (With Plate)
Gilded
65mm
Traces of gilding. Basic
design.
£10 - £15

M12-0408
Buckle (With Plate)
Engraved
80mm
Even patina.
Engraved design on plate.
£15 - £20

M12-0409
Buckle (With Plate)
Gilded
60mm
Traces of gilding.
Pin missing.
£5 - £10

M12-0410
Buckle (With Plate)
34mm
Smooth, even green patina.
Of typical style.
£20 - £30

M12-0411
Buckle (With Plate) Gilded
40mm
Traces of gilding.
Lis design on plate.
£25 - £35

M12-0412
Buckle (With Plate)
58mm
Crowned head (of a king?).
Buckle with its plate.
£40 - £50

M12-0413
Buckle
77mm
Traces of gilding. Unusual type.
£20 - £30

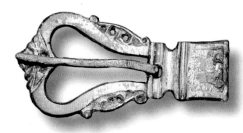

M12-0414
Buckle
80mm
Openwork design. Silvered surface.
£100 - £120

M13-0101
Clothes Fastener
(Bronze)
30mm
Even patina. Basic style.
£20 - £30

M13-0102
Clothes Fastener
(Bronze)
24mm
Standard design. Surface a little uneven.
£15 - £20

M13-0103
Clothes Fastener (Bronze)
54mm
Very large size. Letters "A" and
"H" separated by a ribbon design.
£50 - £60

M13-0104
Fastener (Lead) With
Inscription
34mm
Unusual fastener with
an inscription around.
£80 - £90

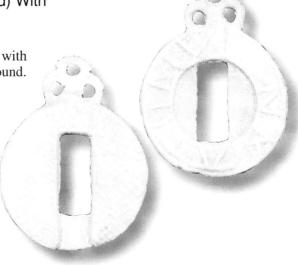

M13-0201
Silver Clothes Fastener
(Gilded)
25mm
Square fixing bar at the back.
Most of the gilding remaining.
£70 - £80

M13-0202
Silver Clothes Fastener
(Gilded)
20mm
Rose-like design in the centre.
£65 - £75

M13-0203
Silver Clothes Fastener
(Gilded)
22mm
Clover leaf shape. Most of the
gilding remaining.
£75 - £80

M13-0204
Silver Clothes Fastener
31mm
Large fastener. Very elaborate
and gilded.
£100 - £120

M13-0205
Silver Clothes Fastener
(Gilded)
36mm
Fully gold gilded. Very large.
£120 - £150

M13-0206
Silver Clothes Fastener
(Gilded)
22mm
Pretty petalled flower design in
the centre.
£80 - £100

M13-0207
Silver Clothes Fastener
20mm
Basic style. Letter "P" engraved.
£70 - £80

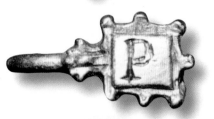

M13-0208
Silver Clothes Fastener
(Gilded)
25mm
Rose design in the centre.
£60 - £70

M13-0209
Silver Clothes Fastener (Gilded)
21mm
Fully gold gilded.
Six domes surrounded by filigree.
£80 - £100

M14-0101
Mirror Case (Complete)
45mm dia
Working condition.
Surface a little pitted.
£75 - £85

M14-0102
Mirror Case (Complete)
45mm dia
Working condition.
£80 - £90

M14-0201
Bodkin (Silver)
133mm
Decorated. Has an ear scoop at
the eye end. Initials "AT" and
dated 1662.
£200 - £250

M14-0202
Ear-Scoop (Silver) Gilt
41mm
Twisted design with pellets.
£60 - £70

M15-0101
Iron Spur
155mm
Good state of preservation.
Rowel in place and buckles
attached.
£90 - £125

M15-0102
Iron Spur
130mm
Good state of preservation.
Prick spur type. Decorated.
£100 - £125

M15-0103
Iron Spur
150mm
Complete with buckle and rowel.
Good state of preservation.
£100 - £125

M16-0101
Lead Seal (Round)
34mm dia
Lis in centre. Weak in places.
Surface a little scuffed.
£20 - £25

M16-0102
Lead Seal (Round)
30mm dia
Lis in centre. Sharp detail.
Suspension loop intact.
£30 - £35

M16-0103
Lead Seal (Round)
25mm dia
Petal in centre. Good, sharp
detail. Even surface.
£30 - £40

M16-0104
Lead Seal (Round)
34mm dia
Sailing boat in centre. Sharp
detail. Rare type.
£50 - £60

M16-0105
Lead Seal (Oval)
36mm
Sharp detail. Large size.
£25 - £30

M16-0106
Lead Seal (Vessica)
30mm
Lis in centre. Detail a little
weak. Surface ragged.
£10 - £15

M16-0107
Lead Seal (Vessica)
32mm
Lis in centre. Sharp detail.
Even surface.
£30 - £35

M16-0108
Lead Seal (Round)
27mm dia
Square and cross in the centre.
Suspension loop on back.
£30 - £40

M16-0109
Lead Seal (Round)
41mm
Winged beast in the centre.
Surface a little rough.
£20 - £25

M16-0110
Seal (Lead)
30mm dia
Petal design in the centre. Sharp
detail.
£30 - £35

M16-0111
Lead Seal (Lion)
32mm
Lion in the centre. Sharp detail.
£35 - £40

M16-0112
Lead Seal (Vessica)
35mm
Good surface. Lis in the centre.
£30 - £35

M16-0201
Bronze Seal (Round)
23mm dia
Letter "B" in centre. Even
patina.
£60 - £70

M16-0202
Bronze Seal (Round)
22mm dia
Crowned letter "I". Patina
a little patchy.
£50 - £60

M16-0203
Bronze Seal (Round)
20mm dia
Merchant's marks within
the shield. Even patina.
£50 - £60

M16-0204
Bronze Seal (Round)
20mm dia
Figure blowing a horn and seated on an animal. Sharp detail. Even patina.

£70 - £80

M16-0205
Bronze Seal (Round)
22mm dia
Leaping stag. Sharp detail. Even patina.

£80 - £100

M16-0206
Bronze Seal (Round)
20mm dia
Monkey-like animal. Detail a little weak.

£70 - £80

M16-0207
Bronze Seal (Round)
19mm dia
Stag's head. Smooth
even patina. Sharp detail.
£80 - £100

M16-0208
Bronze Seal (Round)
23mm dia
Bird in a tree together with
a human head. Sharp
detail. Even surface and
patina.
£100 - £125

M16-0209
Bronze Seal (Round)
20mm dia
Surface a little pitted.
Lis above clasped hands.
Weak detail in places.
£60 - £70

M16-0210
Bronze Seal (Round)
27mm dia
Five leaves. Surface a little uneven. Loop at top.
£75 - £85

M16-0211
Bronze Seal (Round)
22mm dia
Sacrificial lamb. Good, sharp detail. Even patina.
£80 - £90

M16-0212
Bronze Seal (Round)
70mm dia
Very sharp detail. Good, even surface. Complete and undamaged. Large size. Rare.
From £10,000

M16-0213
Bronze Seal (Oval)
28mm
St. Margaret spearing a dragon. Sharp detail. Even patina.
£200 - £250

M16-0214
Bronze Seal
(Vessica Shape)
33mm
Hawk on a glove. Weak detail in places. A little damage on the edges.
£125 - £150

M16-0215
Bronze Seal
(Vessica Shape)
30mm
Bird with a worm in its mouth. Good, sharp detail. Even patina.
£150 - £200

M16-0216
Bronze Seal (Vessica Shape)
31mm
Bird with a branch or twig in its mouth. Very sharp detail. Even patina. Personal name.
£250 - £300

M16-0217
Bronze Seal (Vessica Shape)
31mm
Lion advancing. Very sharp detail. Complete and undamaged. Personal name.
£250 - £300

M16-0218
Bronze Seal (Vessica Shape)
29mm
Sacrificial lamb. Even patina. Smooth surface.
£80 - £90

M16-0219
Bronze Seal
(Vessica Shape)
30mm
Sacrificial lamb.
Sharp detail.
Even patina.
Personal name.
£200 - £250

M16-0220
Bronze Seal (Shield
Shape)
35mm
Bird of prey. Detail a little weak. Personal name.
£175 - £200

M16-0221
Bronze Seal (Shield
Shape)
26mm
Rampant lion. Sharp detail. Good, smooth patina.
£120 - £150

M16-0222
Bronze Seal (Shield Shape)
40mm
Castle or abbey with lis above. Smooth surface. Large size. Personal name.
£300 - £350

M16-0223
Seal (Heraldic)
30mm
Surface a little ragged. Personal name.
£150 - £200

M16-0224
Seal (Bronze)
32mm
Letter "I" in the centre of a pentangle. No inscription.
£70 - £80

M16-0225
Bronze Seal (Round)
19mm
Four leaf clover. Sharp
detail. Even patina.
£120 - £140

M16-0226
Bronze Seal
(Personal)
18mm dia
Smooth surface. Even
patina. Personal name.
Rare type.
£300 - £350

M16-0227
Bronze Seal (Lion)
20mm dia
Even patina. Sleeping
lion in the centre, motto
around.
£120 - £150

M16-0228
Bronze Seal (Round)
31mm dia
Large personal seal. Smooth, even surface. Good patina.

From £800

M16-0229
Bronze Seal (Round)
20mm dia
Sharp detail. Surface a little rough. Personal name.

£300 - £350

M16-0230
Bronze Seal (Round)
18mm dia
Even patina. Head of John the Baptist. Motto around.

£100 - £130

M16-0231
Bronze Seal (Round)
19mm dia
Smooth, even patina. Depicting a bow and arrow. Crescent and star in field. Motto around. Scarce type.
£150 - £200

M16-0232
Bronze Seal (Round)
20mm dia
Squirrel in the centre. Personal name around.
£225 - £275

M16-0233
Bronze Seal (Round)
19mm dia
Smooth, rich patina. Coat of arms in centre. Personal name around.
£250 - £300

M16-0234
Bronze Seal (Round)
17mm dia
Head of John the Baptist
in the centre.
Motto around.
£120 - £150

M16-0235
Bronze Seal (Round)
personal
25mm
Implements or tools in the centre.
Personal name around.
Scarce type.
£250 - £300

M16-0236
Bronze Seal
25mm
Coat of arms in the centre.
No inscription.
£90 - £125

M16-0237
Bronze Seal (Round)
19mm
Small seal. Squirrel in
centre. Motto around.
£70 - £90

M16-0238
Bronze Seal (Round)
20mm dia
Hunting seal. Rabbit over a
dog. Motto around.
£120 - £150

M16-0239
Bronze Seal (Round)
25mm
Very sharp detail. Smooth,
even surface. Lis in centre.
Personal name around.
£250 - £300

M16-0240
Bronze Seal (Round)
23mm
Patina a little patchy.
Bird in the centre.
Motto around.

£90 - £110

M16-0241
Bronze Seal (Round)
32mm high x
25mm dia
Smooth, even surface.
Coat of arms. Decoration
around.

£650 - £750

M16-0242
Bronze Seal (3 Heads)
28mm
Three outwards facing
heads in the centre. Motto
around. Scarce type.

£200 - £250

M16-0243
Bronze Seal (Stag)
20mm dia
Stag in the centre. Motto
around. Traces of iron at the
suspension loop.
£90 - £110

M16-0244
Seal (Bronze)
18mm
Even patina. Clasped hands.
Motto around. Sharp detail.
£80 - £90

M16-0245
Bronze Seal (Personal)
21mm dia
Monogram in the centre.
Personal name around.
Good patina.
£110 - £130

M16-0246
Bronze Seal (Round)
22mm dia
Flat with loop on the back. Head
in the centre. Motto around.
£120 - £150

M16-0247
Bronze Seal (Round)
32mm
Large, flat seal. Loop on the
back. Coat of arms in the
centre. Place name around.
Surface a little pitted.
£150 - £200

M16-0248
Bronze Seal (Round)
19mm dia
Flat with loop on back. Sharp
detail. Personal name around
(cleric).
£175 - £200

M16-0249
Bronze Seal (Round)
22mm
Patina flaking in places. Flat with loop on back. Motto around.
£100 - £120

M16-0250
Bronze Seal
(Hawk On Glove)
18mm dia
Surface a little rough. Personal name around.
£120 - £150

M16-0251
Bronze Seal
(St. Katherine)
26mm
Large size. Sharp detail. St. Katherine in centre. Personal name around.
£250 - £300

M16-0252
Bronze Seal
(Vessica)
28mm
Dodo-like bird in the centre.
Personal name around. Smooth,
even surface. Sharp detail.
£275 - £300

M16-0253
Bronze Seal
(Vessica Shape)
28mm
Dog chasing hare in the centre.
Hunting cry or motto around.
£125 - £150

M16-0254
Bronze Seal
(Vessica Shape)
32mm
Large size. Bird feeding its
young in the centre.
Personal name around.
£250 - £300

M16-0255
Bronze Seal
(Vessica Shape)
30mm
Pelican in her piety in the
centre. Motto around.

£110 - £140

M16-0256
Bronze Seal (Vessica)
28mm
Bird feeding its young in the
centre. Personal name around.

£130 - £170

M16-0257
Seal (Vessica)
42mm
Large size. Detail a little weak.
Bull in the centre. Motto around.

£200 - £250

M16-0258
Bronze Seal
(Vessica Shape)
31mm
Sharp detail. Mary and child in a
canopy. Figure praying beneath.
Personal name around.

£300 - £350

M16-0259
Bronze Seal (Monastic)
49mm
Large priory seal. Slight damage
at the bottom. Sharp detail.

From £1,100

M16-0260
Bronze Seal (Monastic)
50mm
Large monastic or abbey seal.
Patina flaking in places.

From £1,000

M16-0301
Silver Seal (Vessica Shape)
50mm
Virgin Mary with infant. Very sharp detail. Complete and undamaged. Large size. Rare.
P.O.A.

M16-0302
Silver Seal (Vessica Shape)
60mm
Bishop under a canopy, hand of God above. Detail a little weak. Large size. Rare.
From £3,000

M16-0303
Silver Seal (Vessica Shape)
26mm
Silver seal with a Roman intaglio set in the centre. Motto around. Slight damage to the intaglio. Rare.
From £1,200

M16-0401
Papal Bulla
(Lead)
35mm dia
Good detail.
Even colour.
£75 - £85

M16-0402
Papal Bulla
(Lead)
38mm dia
Even colour. A
few scuff marks.
Pierced in the
centre.
£50 - £60

M16-0403
Papal Bulla
(Lead)
39mm dia
One of the faces
scuffed. Sharp
lettering.
£60 - £70

M16-0404
Papal Bulla
(Lead)
38mm dia
Even colour.
Sharp detail on the
faces.
£80 - £90

M16-0405
Papal Bulla
(Lead)
37mm dia
A little pitted on
the surface. Even
colour.
£75 - £85

M16-0406
Papal Bulla
(Lead)
38mm dia
Scuffed in places.
Good detail.
£75 - £85

M16-0407
Papal Bulla (Lead)
40mm dia
Faces a little weak.
£50 - £60

M16-0408
Papal Bulla (Lead)
36mm dia
Scratches and scuffs
over the surface.
£40 - £50

M16-0409
Papal Bulla
38mm
Perfect condition.
Piece of original rope
still running through
the centre.
£100 - £125

M16-0410
Papal
Bulla/Personal
Seal
38mm
Papal bulla with
seal. Engraved on
the reverse. Rare.
£100 - £125

M16-0501
Bag or Sack Seal
25mm dia
Crowned roses.
Complete.
£15 - £20

M16-0502
Bag Or Sack
Seal
41mm
Three crowns for
Bury St. Edmunds.
A little mis-shapen.
£30 - £40

M17-0101
Bronze Key
110mm
Good even patina.
Complete and
undamaged.
£175 - £225

M17-0102
Bronze Key
100mm
Good even patina.
Complete and
undamaged.
£175 - £225

M17-0103
Bronze Key
100mm
Undamaged with even
patina.
£140 - £160

M17-0104
Bronze Key
85mm
Surface a little patchy.
Complete.
£150 - £175

M17-0105
Bronze Key
84mm
Even patina. Plain style.
£90 - £100

M17-0106
Bronze Key
90mm
Surface a little patchy. Plain style.
£70 - £80

M17-0107
Bronze Key
80mm
Good even patina. Chunky size. Rare.
£250 - £300

M17-0108
Bronze Key
95mm
Smooth even patina. Typical style.
£100 - £125

M17-0109
Bronze Key
88mm
Smooth even patina.
Complete and
undamaged.
£175 - £200

M17-0110
Bronze Key
85mm
Surface a little patchy.
Unusual style.
£80 - £100

M17-0111
Bronze Key
95mm
Even patina.
Complete.
£125 - £150

M17-0112
Bronze Key
90mm
Smooth even patina.
Handle well worn.
£90 - £100

M17-0113
Bronze Key
99mm
Even patina.
Unusual style.
£110 - £130

M17-0114
Bronze Key
90mm
Even patina.
Typical style.
£80 - £100

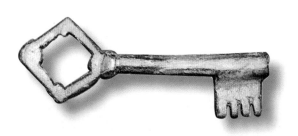

M17-0115
Bronze Key
85mm
Light green,
even patina.
Plain style.
£60 - £80

M17-0116
Bronze Key
85mm
Surface a little
rough. Plain
style.
£60 - £80

M17-0117
Bronze Key
80mm
Even, green patina.
Surface a little uneven.
Unusual type.
£150 - £175

M17-0118
Bronze Key
80mm
Patina a little patchy in
places.
£100 - £120

M17-0119
Bronze Key
114mm
Large key. Surface
a little rough.
Typical style.
£100 - £125

M17-0120
Bronze Key
47mm
Suspension loop at the top.
Simple style. Even patina.
£30 - £40

M17-0121
Bronze Key (Barrel Lock)
58mm
Barrel lock key.
Smooth, even surface.
£40 - £50

M17-0201
Iron Key
124mm
Good state of
preservation.
Large size.
£70 - £80

M17-0202
Iron Key
122mm
Good state of
preservation.
Large size.
Plain style.
£60 - £70

M17-0203
Iron Key
128mm
Good state of
preservation.
Plain style.
£50 - £60

M17-0204
Iron Key
95mm
Good state of preservation.
Plain style.
£50 - £60

M17-0205
Iron Key
80mm
Complete. Very plain.
£30 - £40

M17-0206
Iron Keys
65mm
Good state of
preservation. Small
sizes.
£30 - £40 each

M17-0207
Iron Key
95mm
Good state of
preservation.
£40 - £50

M17-0208
Iron Key
97mm
Large iron key.
Good state of preservaton.
£40 - £50

M17-0301
Casket Keys
Bronze
44mm
Undamaged.
Good even patina.
£10 - £15 each

M17-0302
Casket Key
35mm
Smooth, even surface and
patina.
£40 - £50

M17-0401
Barrel Lock (With Key)
Bronze
70mm
Surface a little ragged.
£60 - £70

M17-0402
Bronze Barrel Lock
36mm
Even patina. Complete.
£60 - £70

M17-0403
Bronze Barrel Lock (Horse)
42mm
Barrel lock in the form of
a pack horse. Rare.
£150 - £200

M17-0501
Ball Lock (Iron)
30mm
Good state of preservation.
Working order.
£70 - £80

M18-0101
Coin Weight (Angel)
15mm
Square shaped. Surface a little
uneven.
£10 - £15

M18-0102
Coin Weight
15mm
Square shaped. Surface a little
ragged.
£10 - £15

M18-0103
Coin Weight (Gold Noble)
18mm dia
Even patina. Detail a little
weak.
£15 - £20

M18-0104
Coin Weight (Gold Noble)
19mm
Circular shape with sharp
detail. Even patina.
£20 - £25

M18-0105
Coin Weight (Noble)
16mm dia
Gold noble weight.
Clear detail.
£20 - £25

M18-0106
Coin Weight
15mm dia
Bronze weight. Even patina.
Crowned lis.
£12 - £15

M18-0107
Coin Weight (Angel)
15mm
Good patina. Nice sharp
detail. Gold angel weight.
£25 - £30

M18-0108
Coin Weight
15mm
Even patina.
Nice, clear detail.
£15 - £18

M18-0109
Coin Weight
14mm
Even patina. Clear detail.
£15 - £18

M18-0201
Trade Weight (Lead) Lion
36mm
Good detail. Undamaged.
Four ounce weight.
£40 - £50

M18-0202
Trade Weight (Lead)
Crowned Lis
70mm
Good detail. A few scuffs.
Eight ounce weight.
£70 - £80

M18-0203
Trade Weight (Lead)
Three Lions
70mm
Fair detail. A few scuffs.
Eight ounce weight.
£65 - £75

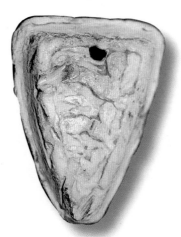

M18-0204
Trade Wieght (Henry VII)
70mm dia
Crowned "H" stamped on the surface. Even patina. Large size.
£35 - £50

M18-0205
Steelyard Weight (Bronze) Lead Filled
70mm
Spherical with a suspension loop. Four shields engraved around the surface. Rare.
£500 - £600

M18-0206
Steelyard Weight (Bronze) Lead Filled
48mm
Spherical. Lead filled. Depicting four lions. Suspension loop missing.
£250 - £300

M18-0207
Trade Weight (4oz)
60mm
Four ounce weight. Bronze.
Good patina. (Henry VII?)
£30 - £35

M18-0208
Trade Weight (2oz)
Elizabeth 1st
46mm dia
Scarce two ounce Elizabeth I
trade weight.
£50 - £60

M18-0209
Trade Weight (Lead)
Three Lions
60mm
Eight ounce weight. A few
scuffs. Good detail.
£70 - £80

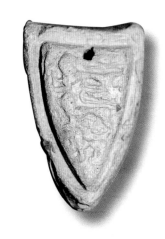

M18-0210
Trade Weight (Lead) 2lb
100mm
Rare two pound weight.
A little scuffed and weak
detail.

£40 - £50

M18-0211
Lead Trade Weight
70mm
Crowned lis. Good detail.
Eight ounce weight.

£70 - £80

M18-0212
Lead Trade Weight
63mm
A few scuffs. Crowned lis.

£50 - £60

M18-0213
Lead Trade Weight
38mm
Small weight. Poor condition.
£10 - £15

M18-0214
Lead Trade Weight
48mm
Unusual type. In the form of a
St. Andrew's cross.
£30 - £40

M18-0215
Trade Weight (Lead)
Cross
60mm
Cross in the centre. Three pellets around.
£25 - £30

M18-0216
Trade Weight (Lead) 1lb
78mm
Heavy pound weight. Possibly
embossed with merchant's
marks.
£40 - £50

M18-0217
Trade Weight (Lead)
35mm
Small weight. Weak detail.
£8 - £10

M18-0218
Trade Weight (Lead) ¹/²lb
55mm
Half pound weight.
"M" or "W" in the centre.
£30 - £35

M18-0219
Trade Weight (Lead) 1lb
55mm
St. Andrew's cross design.
A little scuffed. Weak detail.
£15 - £20

M18-0220
Trade Weight (Lead)
35mm
Four ounce weight. Lion in
centre. Weak detail.
£15 - £20

M18-0221
Trade Weight (Lead)
32mm
Small one ounce weight.
Good detailed lis in centre.
£20 - £25

M18-0222
Trade Weight (Lis)
38mm
Surface a little pitted.
Lead weight.
Lis in centre.

£8 - £10

M18-0301
Balance Arm
84mm
Plain type. Even patina.

£60 - £70

M18-0302
Balance Arm
103mm
Nice, even patina.
Zoomorphic ends to the arms.

£120 - £150

M18-0303
Tumbrell (Coin Balance)
85mm
Rare tumbrel. A little damage on the balance arm. Full museum report.
£400 - £500

M21-0101
Pouring Spout
75mm
Good, smooth surface. Even patina.
£45 - £50

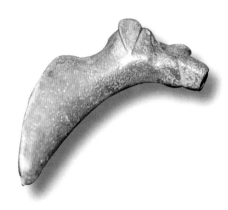

M21-0102
Pouring Spout
75mm
Surface a little pitted. Patchy patina.
£35 - £40

M21-0103
Pouring Spout
75mm
Typical form. Surface a little pitted. Patchy patina.
£30 - £40

M21-0104
Pouring Spout
65mm
Good style. Even patina.
£45 - £50

M21-0105
Pouring Spout
120mm
Elongated neck. Even patina.
£40 - £45

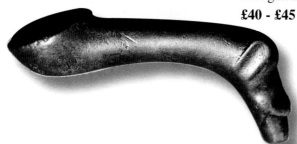

M21-0201
Silver Spoon (c.1629)
Slip Top
165mm
A little damage to the bowl.
Good, clear hallmarks.
From £200

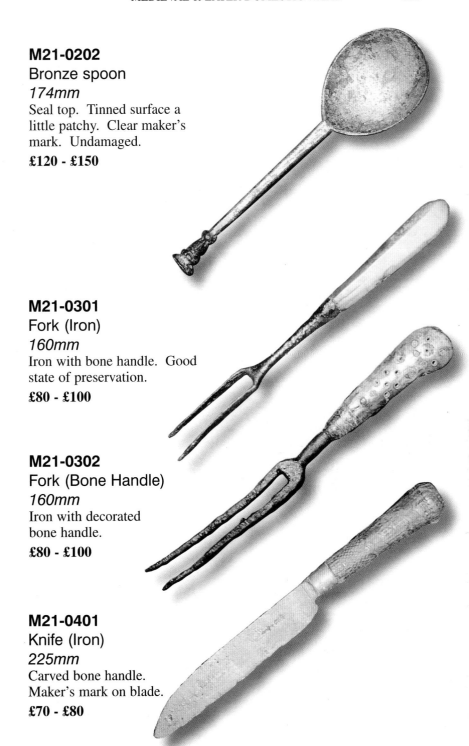

M21-0202
Bronze spoon
174mm
Seal top. Tinned surface a little patchy. Clear maker's mark. Undamaged.
£120 - £150

M21-0301
Fork (Iron)
160mm
Iron with bone handle. Good state of preservation.
£80 - £100

M21-0302
Fork (Bone Handle)
160mm
Iron with decorated bone handle.
£80 - £100

M21-0401
Knife (Iron)
225mm
Carved bone handle. Maker's mark on blade.
£70 - £80

M23-0101
Jetton
(Counter)
25mm dia
Burgundian steel
and flints type.
From £30

M23-0102
Jetton
(Counter)
25mm dia
Crown type.
From £10

M23-0103
Jetton
(Counter)
25mm dia
Dolphin type.
From £10

M23-0104
Jetton
(Counter)
25mm dia
Shield and lis
type.
From £10

M23-0105
Jetton
(Counter)
20mm dia
English. Crude
face type.
From £15

M23-0106
Jetton (Counter)
17mm dia
English. Edward
1st portrait type.
From £15

M23-0201
Boy Bishop Token
(Lead)
28mm
Bishop's mitre.
Groat size.
£15 - £20

M23-0202
Boy Bishop Token
(Lead)
25mm dia
Bishop's head.
Groat size.
£15 - £20

M23-0203
Boy Bishop Token
(Lead)
15mm dia
Bishop's mitre.
Half groat size.
£10 - £15

M23-0204
Boy Bishop Token
(Lead)
28mm dia
Bishop's head. Groat
size. Sharp detail.
£20 - £25

M23-0205
Token (Boy
Bishop) Lead
28mm dia
Groat size. Facing
bust. Sharp detail.
£25 - £30

M23-0206
Token (Boy
Bishop) Lead
28mm dia
Groat size.
Bishop's head.
£15 - £20

M23-0207
Boy Bishop Token
(Bury St. Edmunds)
28mm dia
Three crowns of Bury St.
Edmunds. Groat size.
Slight damage.

£20 - £25

M23-0208
Boy Bishop Token
(Lead)
32mm dia
Large groat size.
Bishop's mitre.

£15 - £20

M23-0209
Boy Bishop Token
(Lead)
25mm dia
Groat size.
Bishop's mitre.

£10 - £15

M23-0210
Lead Token (Elizabeth 1st)
23mm dia
Portrait of Elizabeth I.
Hole pierced through the centre.

£20 - £30

M23-0301
Figurine (Lead)
80mm
Figure of a lady. Possibly a
child's plaything. Scarce.
£70 - £80

M24-0101
Pilgrim Badge
38mm
Virgin Mary badge with pin.
£70 - £80

M24-0102
Pilgrim Badge
35mm
Complete and undamaged with
pin.
£100 - £125

M24-0103
Pilgrim Badge
(Tau Cross)
38mm
Complete and undamaged with
pin.
£100 - £125

M24-0104
Pilgrim Badge
(Virgin Mary)
24mm
Associated with the shrine at
Walsingham. Undamaged with
pin.
£80 - £100

M24-0105
Pilgrim Badge
(Virgin Mary)
22mm
Associated with the shrine at
Walsingham. A little damage.
No pin.
£50 - £60

M24-0106
Pilgrim Badge (Virgin
Mary)
24mm
Associated with the shrine
at Walsingham. A little
damage. With pin.
£60 - £70

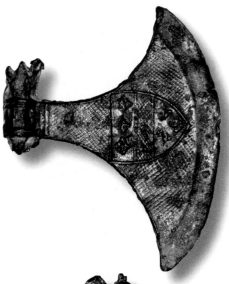

M24-0107
Pilgrim Badge (Axe)
67mm
Good example. Sharp detail.
£120 - £140

M24-0108
Pilgrim Badge
(Bromholm)
44mm
Sacred hart badge with pin
intact.
£125 - £150

M24-0109
Pilgrim Badge
(Scabbard)
58mm
Associated with Fitz Urse,
leader of the knights who
attacked Becket. Pin intact.
£150 - £200

M24-0110
Pilgrim Badge (Thomas
Becket)
88mm
Complete with pin. "Thomas"
at the base. Large size.
From £400

M24-0111
Pilgrim Badge
(St. Leonard)
50mm
Undamaged and complete with
pin. Of the finest quality.
From £600

M24-0112
Pilgrim Badge
(St. Leonard)
45mm
Complete with pin.
Slight damage.
Banner missing from base.
From £300

M24-0113
Pilgrim Badge
50mm
Scarce badge. Horse's front
legs missing. Pin intact.
£250 - £300

M24-0114
Pilgrim Badge (Bronze)
28mm
Sew-on type. A little damage.
£50 - £70

M24-0115
Badge (Bronze)
23mm
Loop on the back.
Even patina.
£60 - £70

M24-0116
Pilgrim Badge
(Thomas Becket)
55mm
Pewter badge. Good detail.
Most of pin remaining.
£350 - £400

M24-0117
Badge (Bronze)
25mm
Small figure in the centre.
Flanked by another figure on
each side.
£50 - £60

M24-0118
Pilgrim Badge
55mm
Pewter bell suspended
from a chain.
£50 - £60

M24-0119
Pilgrim Badge
80mm
Pewter letter "M"
suspended from a chain.
£60 - £70

M24-0120
Pilgrim Badge
19mm dia
Possibly head of John the
Baptist. Slight damage.
£30 - £40

M24-0121
Pilgrim Badge
56mm
Pewter crucifix. Sew on
badge.
£150 - £175

M24-0122
Pilgrim Badge
40mm
Advancing archer. Damaged in places.
£110 - £130

M24-0123
Pilgrim Badge (Lead)
25mm
Head of Thomas Becket.
£15 - £20

M24-0124
Pilgrim Badge (St. George)
20mm
St. George's cross. Badge with pin.
£40 - £50

M24-0125
Pilgrim Badge (Bellows)
22mm
Badge in the form of bellows.
With pin.
£50 - £60

M24-0126
Pilgrim Badge
(Ostrich Feather)
58mm
A little ragged around the
edges. Large size.
£70 - £80

M24-0127
Retainer's badge
(Talbot Dog)
35mm
In the form of a talbot which
was a hunting dog. With pin.
£80 - £90

M24-0128
Pilgrim Badge (Becket)
40mm
Openwork with Thomas Becket's
head in the centre.
Slight damage. With pin.
£110 - £130

M24-0129
Pilgrim Badge
55mm
Knight on horseback.
Badge with pin.
£100 - £125

M24-0130
Pilgrim Badge
48mm
Large badge.
"IHS" in the centre.
With pin.
£120 - £150

M24-0131
Pilgrim Badge (Phallus)
63mm
A walking phallus badge.
Surface a little ragged.
Large size.
£120 - £150

M24-0132
Pilgrim Badge
(Poppinjay)
48mm
Slight damage.
Feet missing. With pin.
£70 - £80

M24-0133
Pilgrim Badge
38mm
Badge in the form of a
crown. Small piece broken
at the top.
£60 - £70

M24-0134
Retainer's Badge
24mm
In the form of a barrel lock
(Henry VII). With pin.
£100 - £120

M24-0135
Pilgrim Badge
40mm
Sew on type openwork frame.
Mary and child in the centre.
£100 - £125

M24-0136
Pilgrim Badge
34mm
Double sided badge. Probably
worn as a pendant.
£125 - £150

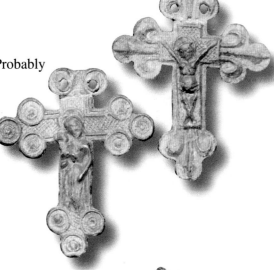

M24-0137
Pilgrim Badge
(Walsingham)
25mm
Virgin Mary and child.
Complete with pin.
£100 - £130

M24-0138
Pilgrim Badge (Henry VI)
30mm
Badge associated with Henry VI. Lozenge shape. Piece missing at the top. With pin.
£150 - £175

M24-0139
Pilgrim Badge
22mm
In the form of a crossbow. With its pin.
£60 - £70

M24-0140
Pilgrim Badge (Punctured Heart)
24mm
In the form of a punctured heart. With pin.
£70 - £80

M24-0141
Pilgrim Badge (Lis)
22mm
Complete with pin.
£30 - £40

M24-0142
Pilgrim Badge
(Gloves of Becket)
19mm
Representing the gloves of
Thomas Becket. With pin.
£80 - £100

M24-0143
Pilgrim Badge
(Gloves of Becket)
18mm
Representing the gloves of
Thomas Becket. With pin.
£80 - £100

M24-0144
Pilgrim Badge (Slippers)
Walsingham
20mm
Slippers associated with the shrine at Walsingham. With pin.
£70 - £90

M24-0145
Badge (Retainer's)
45mm
Lion passant. Large sew on type. One eyelet broken away.
£120 - £150

M24-0146
Pilgrim Badge
23mm
Bird feeding its young (pelican in piety). With pin.
£140 - £175

M24-0147
Pilgrim Badge (Fish)
61mm
Silvered surface. With pin. Scarce type.
£80 - £100

M24-0148
Pilgrim Badge
28mm
Seated Mary and child within a
quatrefoil openwork frame.
With pin and undamaged.
£160 - £190

M24-0149
Pilgrim Badge
20mm dia
Petalled flower within an openwork frame. With pin.
£60 - £70

M24-0150
Pilgrim Badge
25mm
Two figures standing
within a letter "M" with pin.
£90 - £120

M24-0151
Pilgrim Badge
27mm
Two figures standing within a
letter "M". With pin.
£80 - £90

M24-0152
Pilgrim Badge
(Peter & Paul)
35mm
Depicting Peter and Paul.
Good clear detail. Scarce type.
£150 - £200

M24-0153
Mount
49mm
A little damaged but sharp
detail. Large size.
£150 - £200

M24-0154
Pilgrim Badge
38mm
Sew on type.
First class condition.
£225 - £275

M24-0155
Pilgrim Badge
23mm
Head within a frame.
Complete with pin.
£50 - £60

M24-0156
Pilgrim Badge
17mm dia
Head within a frame.
Inscription around.
With pin.
£100 - £120

M24-0157
Pilgrim Badge
(St Leonard)
42mm
Slight break in his crozier.
Apart from that a perfect
badge.
£500 - £600

M24-0158
Pilgrim Badge (Henry VI)
51mm
Good size. Slight damage.
With pin.
£120 - £150

M24-0159
Pilgrim Badge
(John Schorn)
42mm
Vicar John Schorn pulling the
devil out of a boot. With pin.
£200 - £300

M24-0201
Ampulla (Pilgrim's) Tin
23mm
One side shows Becket being beheaded. The other shows the head of Becket above a scallop. Small but complete. Rare.
£140 - £160

M24-0202
Ampulla (Pilgrim's) Tin
54mm
Scenes on each side. Reliquary-shaped. Rare.
£250 - £350

M24-0203
Ampulla (Pilgrim's) Lead
45mm
Both lugs present. Basic type.
£25 - £30

M24-0204
Ampulla (Pilgrim's) Lead
52mm
Both lugs present. Even shape.
£40 - £45

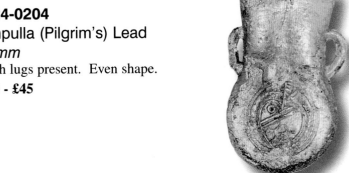

M24-0205
Ampulla (Pilgrim's) Lead
50mm
Both lugs present.
A little mis-shapen.
£25 - £30

M24-0206
Ampulla (Pilgrim's) Lead
48mm
Both lugs present.
Crude animal's head on one
side. A little mis-shapen.
£35 - £40

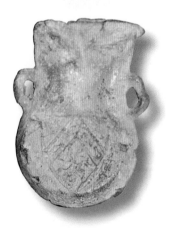

M24-0207
Ampulla (Pilgrim's) Lead
48mm
Both lugs present. Fairly even
shape.
£30 - £35

M24-0208
Ampulla (Pilgrim's) Lead
50mm
Lugs missing. Bag shaped.
Letters on one side.

£40 - £45

M24-0209
Ampulla (Pilgrim's) Lead
50mm
Both lugs present. Good even
shape.

£50 - £60

M24-0210
Ampulla (Pilgrim's) Lead
50mm
Both lugs present. Good even
shape.

£50 - £60

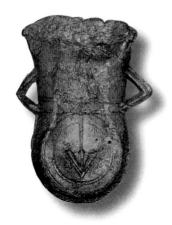

M24-0211
Ampulla (Pilgrim's) Lead
48mm
Both lugs present. A little
ragged at the top.
£30 - £35

M24-0212
Ampulla (Pilgrim's) Lead
52mm
One lug damaged. Face on
one side.
£40 - £45

M24-0213
Ampulla (Pilgrim's) Lead
45mm
Both lugs present. Good even
shape.
£40 - £45

M24-0214
Ampulla (Pilgrim's)
Lead
54mm
Both lugs present.
Good even shape.
Letters on one side.

£50 - £60

M24-0215
Ampulla (Pilgrim's)
Lead
53mm
Both lugs present.
Even shape.

£40 - £45

M24-0216
Ampulla (Pilgrim's)
With Chain
58mm
Good even shape. Both lugs
present. Complete suspen-
sion chain. Very rare.

£150 - £180

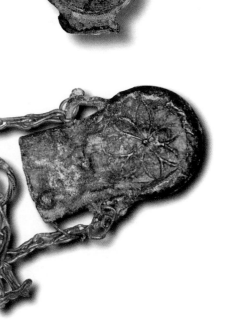

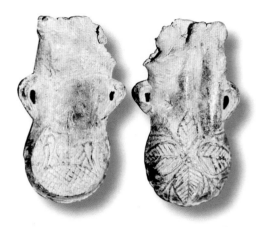

M24-0217
Ampulla (Pilgrim's)
55mm
A little damage.
Both lugs present.
£30 - £35

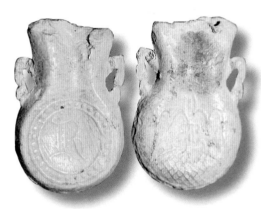

M24-0218
Ampulla (Pilgrim's)
47mm
Both lugs present.
Good, even colour.
£35 - £45

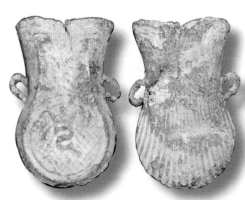

M24-0219
Ampula (Pilgrim's)
Lead
48mm
Crowned reversed "S".
Both lugs present.
£40 - £50

M24-0220
Ampula (Pilgrim's)
Lead
43mm
Letters on both sides.
A little scuffed
in places.
£100 - £120

M24-0221
Pilgrim's Ampula
40mm
Coats of arms on
both sides.
Surface a little flaky.
£90 - £100

M24-0222
Pilgrim's Ampula
(Ewer)
40mm
Unusual ewer shape.
A little dented in places.
£70 - £80

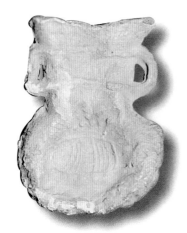

M24-0223
Ampula (Pilgrim's)
46mm
Large size. Both lugs present.
Barrel on one side.
£60 - £70

M24-0224
Ampula (Pilgrim's)
48mm
Ship on one side, cross and
candlesticks on an altar on the
other. Very rare type.
£200 - £250

M24-0225
Ampula (Pilgrim's)
72mm
Amphora shape.
A little ragged in places.
Large.
£60 - £70

M24-0301
Boar Badge (Gilded)
Silver
58mm
Retainer's badge (Richard
III). One leg of boar
missing. Very rare.
£700 - £800

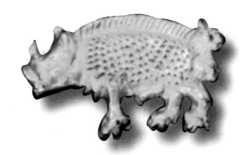

M24-0302
Badge (Lead)
20mm dia
Crude style. Even colour.
£20 - £30

M24-0303
Badge (Silver)
18mm
Small retainer's badge
depicting an owl.
£60 - £70

M24-0304
Badge (Retainer's) Silver Gilt
28mm
Loop on the back. George and dragon. Detail a little worn.
£100 - £120

M24-0305
Staff Top (Pilgrim's)
43mm
Pewter staff top in the form of a bird.
£60 - £70

M24-0306
Pilgrim's Whistle
75mm
Pewter pilgrim's whistle. Undamaged and rare.
£120 - £150

M25-0101
Purse Bar
85mm
Fairly plain design. Smooth, even patina.
£30 - £40

M25-0102
Purse Bar
90mm
Smooth, even patina.
Engraved detail on the surface.
£40 - £50

M25-0103
Purse Bar
90mm
Patina patchy. Silver inlaid "IHS" in the centre.
£65 - £75

M25-0104
Purse Bar
98mm
Twisted knop ends.
Patchy patina.
£20 - £25

M25-0105
Purse Bar
145mm
Long purse bar.
Traces of
silver inlay. Cross
hatch design.
Surface very uneven.
£50 - £60

M25-0106
Purse Bar
(Silver Inlay)
170mm
Good, even patina.
Large size. Most of
the silver inlay
remaining.
£125 - £150

M25-0201
Bronze Thimble
26mm
Even patina. Thick
and chunky style.
£30 - £40

M25-0202
Bronze Thimble
20mm
Chunky and heavy.
Patina a little patchy.
£20 - £30

M25-0203
Thimble (Thumb)
30mm
Large thumb thimble.
Weak patina.
£25 - £30

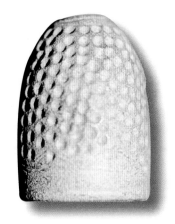

M25-0204
Bronze Thimble
13mm
Beehive thimble.
Even patina.
£20 - £25

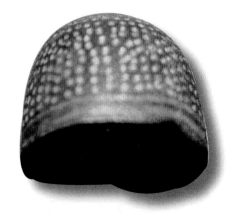

M25-0205
Bronze Thimble
15mm
Beehive thimble.
Uneven surface.
£15 - £20

M25-0206
Bronze Thimble
18mm
Smooth surface.
Even patina.
£25 - £30

M25-0207
Bronze Thimble
14mm
Good, even patina.
Smooth surface.
£25 - £30

M25-0208
Bronze Thimble
20mm
Surface a little pitted.
£15 - £20

M99-0101
Monumental Brass
Plaque
150mm
Two figures praying.
Broken across the centre.
Large and rare.

£500 - £600

M99-0102
Bone Carving (Bishop)
67mm
Rare bone carving of a bishop.
Good state of preservation.

£130 - £150

M99-0201
Part of Purse Frame
(Inscribed)
75mm
Religious inscription.

£10 - £20

M99-0202
Silver Hawking Ring
(Inscribed)
10mm dia
Owner's name engraved around
the outside. Rare.

**From £200 (depending upon
the importance of the owner)**

M99-0203
Silver Hawking Ring
(Inscribed)
9mm dia
Named hawking ring in silver.
£200 - £250

M99-0204
Hawking Ring (Silver)
10mm
Named, with family coat of
arms.
£350 - £400

M99-0301
Casket Cover (Lead)
Reliquary
70mm
Very slight traces of enamel.
Lion with right paw on a
shield. Scarce.
£80 - £100

M99-0302
Casket Handle
(Enamelled) Broken
65mm
Most of the gilding
remaining. Enamelled
heraldic devices. Broken.
£100 - £125

M99-0303
Hanger (Gilded)
Enamelled
58mm
Scarce but surface a little
ragged.
£70 - £80

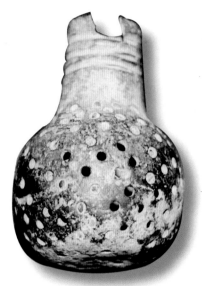

M99-0304
Incense Burner (Bronze)
105mm
Slightly damaged at the top but rare.
£150 - £200

M99-0305
Miniature Cauldron
25mm
Three legged cauldron.
£30 - £40

M99-0401
Lead Bird Seed Holder
75mm
A little uneven but complete.
£30 - £40

M99-0402
Die Tester (Lead)
80mm
Three repeated designs
from the same die.
£70 - £90

M99-0501
Pointer (Silver Gilt)
94mm
Rampant lion. Super detail.
Book pointer or marker,
in silver.
£150 - £200

M99-0502
Page Marker (Bookmark)
60mm
Rare page bookmark with
locking device. Even patina.
£100 - £120

M99-0601
Glazed Tile (Lion)
150mm
Undamaged. Virtually all
glaze remaining.
£80 - £100

M99-0701
Sun Dial
29mm dia
Small but complete bronze
pocket sundial.
£80 - £100

M99-0801
Silver Bodkin
150mm
Long bodkin decorated around
the eye.
£100 - £120

M99-0802
Silver Bodkin
90mm
Has an ear scoop on the end.
With owner's initials and
maker's mark along its body.
£120 - £150

M99-0803
Silver Bodkin
88mm
Plain undecorated.
£50 - £60

M99-0804
Silver Bodkin
120mm
Ear scoop on the end. Also
decorated along three quarters
of its length.
£120 - £150

THE POST-TUDOR YEARS

Civil war and revolution. Republicanism and the suspension of the monarchy. The restoration of monarchy and political division. The emergence of true parliamentarianism. The consolidation of criminal and civil law. 17th and 18th century Britain enjoyed both turbulence and peace. Whilst the history of these years is fascinating, some view their artefacts as not so interesting. There are certainly fewer collectors for this period compared with earlier ages and this is reflected in generally lower values.

However, there is a strong demand for any item relevant to the Commonwealth (Cromwellian) period as well as for good 17th century traders' tokens. These tokens first came into being prior to the seventeenth century when traders and their customers were often dissatisfied with the lack of small denominations of currency when dealing in small amounts of low value commodities. But it was in the middle of the 17th century, when the Royal head was severed, that there was an enormous upsurge in traders issuing their own token in place of currency. Their example was followed by town mayors, overseers of the poor and the wealthy landed gentry. So, today, there is a great market in tokens of many shapes, sizes and issues and in various metals, found regularly by metal detectorists. Collectors take great delight in researching the background to their tokens.

Another item incepting prior to the 17th century but continuing to be manufactured were those beer jugs known as Bellarmines which are now highly collectable. Named as an insult to a Dutch Cardinal, the fashion came to England for creating such beer jugs, usually bearing a grotesque face and sometimes an inscription. Similarly, posy rings continued to be produced and are continuing to be found to the delight of collectors who value the many and varied inscriptions. If love you bear, for me this wear and Noe star to me so bright as thee are far more romantic inscriptions than those chosen by Lady Cathcart and the Bishop of Lincoln in the 18th century. On marrying her fourth husband in 1713, Lady Cathcart's ring was engraved If I survive I will have five. Similarly, John Thomas, the Bishop of Lincoln on marrying his fourth wife chose If I survive I'll make them five.

These were the centuries of flourishing arts and sciences. The fine buildings designed by Christopher Wren and Inigo Jones still stand. The furniture of Thomas Chippendale still furnishes. As well as our own fine artists and musicians, London attracted the finest foreign painters and composers. Despite early Puritan attempts to curtail it, the theatre thrived and, by the end of the 18th century, provincial theatre was commonplace. Navigation equipment was becoming more sophisticated as the science of optics was explored with the resultant and successful lens production. Isaac Newton published his "Principia" in 1687 turning many previously held yet unproven mathematical and physics theories on their head. Literature and literacy grew unchecked until demand led to the opening of public libraries in 1725 and this literature encompassed great works of philosophy by, for example, Jonathan Swift and John Locke.

However, despite such stimulating advances in art and science, metal artefacts are not nearly so stimulating for here we see the advent of mechanisation and mass production. Compare, for example the mass-produced buckles of the 18th century with those of say the Anglo-Saxons and the Vikings. The former could be pretty, the latter could be magnificent. This was the age that saw the advent of machinery taking over from craftsmen.

P04-0101
Iron Knives
70mm
Pen-knife   £40 - £50
Fixed blade £35 - £45

P04-0102
Iron Knife (Bone Handle)
200mm
Decorated handle. Good state
of preservation.
£60 - £70

P04-0103
Iron Knife (Silver Handle)
139mm
Silver decorated handle. Good
state of preservation.
£100 - £125

P04-0104
Folding Knife Handle
71mm
In the form of a squirrel or
beaver. Good detail.
£120 - £150

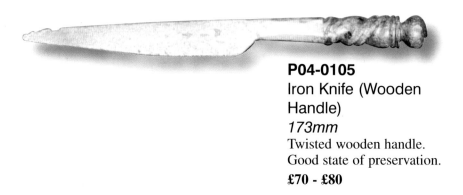

P04-0105
Iron Knife (Wooden Handle)
173mm
Twisted wooden handle. Good state of preservation.
£70 - £80

P04-0106
Iron Knife (Bronze) Inscription
85mm
Bronze handle. Iron blade with inscription on both sides.
£40 - £50

P05-0101
Mace Head (Iron)
164mm
Surface decorated. Four fins around the shaft. Rare.
£300 - £350

P06-0101
Silver Pin (Gilded)
78mm
Openwork designed head.
Most of the gilding remaining.
£80 - £100

P08-0101
Pendant (Silver)
28mm
Engraved initials on
one side. Flower on
the other.
£65 - £80

P08-0102
Pendant (Silver)
28mm
Charles I royalist
badge or pendant.
Good detail.
£150 - £200

P08-0201
Badge (Brass)
30mm
Figure standing by an altar.
Even patina. Fixing lug on
the back.
£40 - £50

P08-0202
Badge (Bracteate)
Brass
38mm dia
Head in the centre
surrounded by an inscription.
A little damage.
£70 - £80

P09-0101
Mount (Head)
65mm
Bearded man wearing a
cloth hat. Even patina.
£60 - £70

P09-0102
Mount (Heraldic)
48mm dia
Three fixing lugs on the back.
Good, even patina.
£80 - £100

P09-0103
Mount (Dog)
80mm
Mount in the form of a talbot
hunting dog.
£25 - £35

P09-0104
Mount (Gilded)
47mm
Mount with inscription.
£80 - £90

P09-0105
Mount (Gilded)
63mm
Large mount in the
form of a gruesome
face.

£50 - £60

P10-0101
Gold Posy Ring
19mm dia
Plain band. A little
mis-shapen.
Inscription on the
inside. Wearable size.

£150 - £200

P10-0102
Gold Posy Ring
14mm dia
Plain band. Inscription
on the inside. Small
size.

£125 - £175

P10-0103
Gold Posy Ring
19mm dia
Plain band. Inscription
on the inside. Good
wearable size and wide
band.

£350 - £400

P10-0104
Gold Posy Ring
15mm dia
Plain band. Inscription on the inside. Thin band. Small size.
£180 - £230

P10-0105
Gold Posy Ring
19mm dia
Plain band. Inscription on the inside. Wearable size.
£200 - £250

P10-0106
Gold Posy Ring
15mm dia
Decorated band and bezel. Inscription on the inside. Small.
£200 - £250

P10-0107
Gold Posy Ring
15mm dia
Plain band. Inscription on the inside. Small size.
£150 - £190

P10-0108
Gold Posy Ring
(8 grammes)
22mm dia
Plain band. Inscription
on the inside. Large,
wearable size.
£400 - £500

P10-0109
Gold Posy Ring
16mm
Decorated band.
Inscription on the
inside. Small size.
£170 - £200

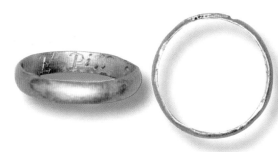

P10-0110
Gold Memorial Ring
18mm
Inscription on the
inside. Skull engraved
on the outside.
£125 - £150

P10-0111
Silver Posy Ring
(Gilded)
17mm dia
Plain band. Inscription
on the inside. Wearable
size.
£100 - £125

P10-0201
Gold Memorial Ring
24mm dia
Inscription on the outside. Large size.

£175 - £200

P10-0202
Gold Ring (Decorated)
16mm dia
Decorated band. Hollow construction. No inscription.

£100 - £125

P10-0203
Gold Ring (Emerald)
16mm dia
Interlaced ribbon design with an emerald setting.

£250 - £300

P10-0204
Memorial Ring (Gold)
Enamelled
19mm
Remains of black enamel. Inscription on the outside and dated.

£200 - £250

P10-0205
Gold Memorial Ring
19mm dia
Heavy ring. Black enamel inlay. Maker's mark and date of 1671.
£300 - £350

P11-0101
Staff Top
60mm
Bearded man wearing a hat. Silvered surface.
£60 - £80

P12-0101
Gold Shoe Buckles (Pair)
38mm
Iron pins. In good working order.
£100 - £125

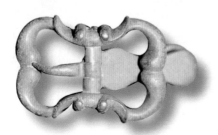

P12-0102
Buckle
38mm
Even patina. Decorative style.
£10 - £15

P12-0103
Silver Buckle (With Maker's Mark)
40mm
Iron rivet still in situ.
Prominent maker's mark.
£30 - £40

P12-0104
Buckle (Gilded) Bronze
57mm
Two opposing lions' heads.
£60 - £70

P13-0101
Button (Head Of Christ)
25mm dia
Good detail. Even patina.
£15 - £20

P13-0102
Button (Silver)
16mm
Two crowned hearts.
£15 - £20

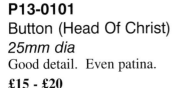

P15-0101
Bridle Boss
65mm dia
Cherub style head
in the centre.
Heads around the
outside.
£50 - £60

P16-0101
Lead Bale Seal
40mm dia
A little scuffed in
places but com-
plete.
£20 - £30

P16-0102
Lead Cloth Seal
(Colchester)
48mm dia
Griffin on one side.
Three ships on the
other.
£60 - £75

P16-0103
Bag or Bale Seal (Lead)
50mm
Sharp detail.
£30 - £40

P16-0104
Bag or Bale Seal (Lead)
20mm
Small size. Complete.
£15 - £20

P16-0105
Bale Seal (Lead)
Commonwealth
17mm dia
Oliver Cromwell period.
Bale seal.
£10 - £15

P16-0106
Bag or Bale Seal (Lead)
23mm
Depiction of Queen Anne.
£10 - £15

P16-0201
Fob Seal (Bronze) Gilded
28mm
Some of the gilding remaining.
Good, undamaged stone.
£50 - £60

P16-0301
Fob Seal (Silver) Queen
Anne
27mm
Seal gives a sharp impression.
Good silver.
£100 - £125

P16-0302
Fob Seal Silver
30mm
Seal gives good, sharp impression. Letters "E" and "A" with a love knot.
£125 - £150

P16-0303
Fob Seal (Silver)
26mm
Heraldic silver fob seal. Loop a little worn.
£80 - £90

P16-0304
Fob Seal (Silver)
23mm
Monogrammed silver fob seal (Robert Hart?).
£100 - £120

P16-0305
Fob Seal (Silver)
36mm high
Monogrammed silver fob
seal.
£70 - £80

P16-0306
Fob Seal (Silver)
Gilded
30mm
Set with an engraved
intaglio.
£40 - £50

P16-0401
Gold Fob Seal
30mm
Coat of arms engraved on
the intaglio. Undamaged.
£200 - £300

P16-0402
Fob Seal (Gold)
22mm
Gold with engraved intaglio setting.
£80 - £100

P17-0101
Casket Key
45mm
Openwork handle. Standard type.
£15 - £20

P17-0102
Casket Key
46mm
Openwork handle. Standard type. Smooth, even patina.
£15 - £20

P17-0103
Iron Latch Key
75mm
Good state of preservation.
£30 - £40

P17-0104
Iron Key
140mm
Good state of preservation.
Large size.
£20 - £30

P18-0101
Lead Weight (Norwich)
Queen Anne
48mm dia
A few scuffs on the surface.
Sharp marks.
£60 - £75

P18-0102
Bronze Weight
50mm dia
Large size. Even patina.
£25 - £30

P18-0103
Bronze Weight
25mm
Surface a little rough.
Good marks.
£30 - £35

P18-0104
Bronze Weight
20mm dia
Even patina. Good, clear
marks. Small.
£15 - £20

P18-0105
Trade Weight (Charles I)
42mm dia
Even patina. Clear marks.
£25 - £30

P18-0106
Trade Weight (Charles I)
45mm dia
Surface a little battered. Four
ounce weight.
£30 - £35

P18-0107
Lead Weight (Charles II)
1/2 oz
23mm dia
Surface a little damaged.
£10 - £15

P18-0108
Lead Weight (James I)
1/4oz
17mm dia
Surface a little uneven.
Clear markings.
£15 - £20

P18-0109
Weight (Charles I) 1/2oz
25mm dia
Crowned "CR" mark.
Half ounce weight.
£15 - £20

P18-0110
Lead weight
(Crowned C)
85mm dia
Large Charles I weight.
£30 - £40

P18-0111
Lead Weight
(Queen Anne)
55mm dia
Crowned "A" for Queen Anne.
Clear markings.
£50 - £60

P18-0112
Bronze Weight
19mm
Good detail. Even patina.
£15 - £20

P18-0113
Bronze Weight
18mm
Clear marking.
Even surface.
£5 - £8

P18-0114
Coin Weight
18mm
Surface a little rough.
Coat of arms design.
£8 - £10

P18-0115
Coin Weight (Charles I)
17mm dia
Charles I coin weight. Clear
legend and portrait.
£15 - £20

P18-0116
Coin Weight (James I)
14mm
Even patina.
Ten shilling weight.
£20 - £25

P18-0117
Coin Weight
(James I) Spur Ryal
18mm
Good, clear markings.
Lacking patina.
£15 - £20

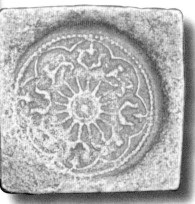

P20-0101
Rumbler Bell
68mm dia
Very large size. Name
engraved on the bottom. Bell
rings.
£80 - £100

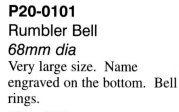

P20-0102
Rumbler Bell
60mm dia
Standard type. Large size.
Bell rings.
£30 - £40

P20-0103
Rumbler Bell
55mm dia
Standard type.
Clear markings. Large size.
£25 - £30

P20-0201
Bronze Bell (Decorated)
40mm
Good, even patina. Leaf design engraved on the surface.
£40 - £50

P20-0202
Bell (Bronze)
48mm
Undamaged.
Embossed hammer on the surface.
£15 - £20

P20-0301
Hawking Whistle (Pewter)
48mm
Dog's head.
£30 - £50

P20-0302
Hawking Whistle (Pewter)
55mm
Dog's head. Suspension loop
underneath.
£50 - £60

P21-0101
Apple Corer (Bone)
140mm
Bronze plate with a name
engraved.
£60   £80

P21-0201
Iron Shears
88mm
Good state of preservation.
Working order.
£75 - £85

P21-0301
Barrel Tap
80mm
Zoomorphic. Even patina.
Undamaged.
£10 - £12

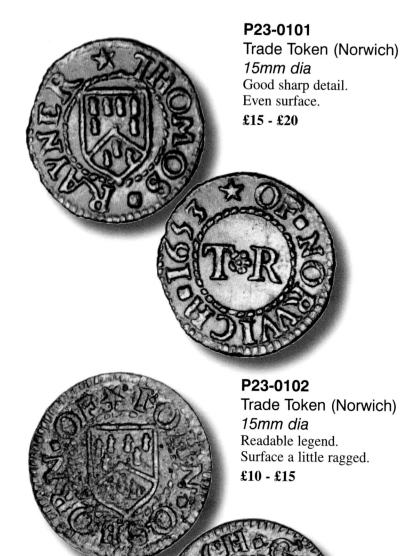

P23-0101
Trade Token (Norwich)
15mm dia
Good sharp detail.
Even surface.
£15 - £20

P23-0102
Trade Token (Norwich)
15mm dia
Readable legend.
Surface a little ragged.
£10 - £15

P23-0103
Trade Token (Beccles)
15mm dia
Sharp detail. Even surface.
£20 - £25

P23-0104
Trade Token (Norwich)
15mm dia
Sharp detail. Even surface.
£15 - £20

P23-0201
Toy Firearm
65mm
Surface a little pitted.
Small size.
£25 - £30

P23-0202
Toy Firearm
90mm
Surface a little uneven.
Large size.
£40 - £50

P23-0203
Toy Firearm
77mm
Even patina.
Broken trigger guard.
£20 - £30

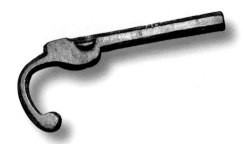

P23-0204
Toy Firearm (Curved Butt)
75mm
Good, even surface.
Unusual curved butt.
Scarce.
£60 - £75

P23-0205
Toy Firearm
78mm
Even patina. Complete.
£60 - £70

P23-0206
Toy Firearm
(With Maker's Mark)
95mm
Good, even patina.
Maker's mark stamped on
the butt. Large size. Rare.
£150 - £175

P23-0207
Toy Firearm
115mm
Good, even surface.
Ramrod in place. Very
large.
£150 - £200

P23-0208
Toy Firearm
76mm
Surface a little uneven.
Complete.
£50 - £65

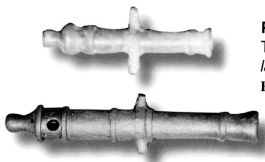

P23-0209
Toy Cannons
largest 90mm
From £10

P23-0210
Toy Cannon
(Whistle)
70mm
Even patina. Toy canon
converted to a whistle.
£30 - £40

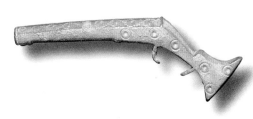

P23-0211
Toy Firearm
90mm
Trigger guard broken.
Decorated along the
barrel and butt.
£25 - £30

P23-0212
Toy Firearm
82mm
Ragged surface.
£15 - £20

P24-0101
Reliquary Cross (Silver)
60mm
Hinged with suspension loop.
Rare.
£150 - £200

P24-0102
Pilgrims Whistle
(Pewter)
82mm
Embossed decoration along its
length. Suspension loop
underneath.
£80 - £100

P25-0101
Silver Thimble
(Charles 1st)
30mm
Oak tree on one side. King
Charles' portrait on the other.
Owner's initials engraved
under the King's head. Rare.
From £750

P25-0102
Silver Thimble
28mm
A little dented in places.
Large size.
£70 - £80

P99-0101
Pipe Tamper (Four
Heads)
59mm
Turn upside down to view
another two heads. Even patina. Complete.
£65 - £75

P99-0102
Combination Ring, Pipe
Tamper & Cork Screw
101mm
Even patina. Large size.
£40 - £50

P99-0103
Pipe Tamper (Dragon)
48mm
Even patina. Complete.
£20 - £30

P99-0104
Combination Tool
(Pipe Tamper etc)
72mm
Good, smooth surface.
Working condition.
Rare.
£100 - £125

P99-0105
Pipe Tamper (Charles I)
70mm
Good detail. Crowned Charles I
on one side. Weaker detail of
his wife on the other.
£120 - £150

P99-0106
Pipe Tamper (Leg)
50mm
Leg wearing a boot.
£15 - £20

P99-0107
Combination Tamper
Ring & Seal
55mm
Even patina.
£15 - £20

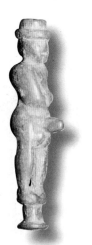

P99-0108
Pipe Tamper
67mm
Naked man wearing a hat.
Even patina.
£40 - £50

P99-0109
Pipe Tamper (Erotic)
65mm
Good detail. Lack of patina.
Depicting a couple copulating.
£100 - £120

P99-0201
Horn Book (Lead)
48mm
Good detail.
Undamaged. Rare.
(Used as teaching aid.)
£150 - £200

P99-0202
Horn Book (Lead)
48mm dia
Clear detail. Circular. Note
letter "T" comes after "W".
Rare. (Used as teaching aid).
£175 - £225

P99-0203
Perpetual Calender
37mm dia
Bronze. Clear detail.
£15 - £20

P99-0204
Cock Spur (Silver)
34mm
Rare fighting cock spur.
£80 - £100